The Garlands of Rampur

Rampur Police: The District Superintendent, Albert Cartwright (seated centre), and Inspectors.

The Garlands of Rampur

Jill Cartwright

The Pentland Press
Edinburgh – Cambridge – Durham – USA

First published in 1998 by
The Pentland Press Ltd
1 Hutton Close,
South Church
Bishop Auckland
Durham

ISBN 1-85821-549-8

Typeset by Carnegie Publishing, 18 Maynard St, Preston
Printed and bound by Bookcraft Ltd, Bath

*For my mother and father
who loved and served India,
and for those who have shared
their experiences.*

Contents

Illustrations

Acknowledgements

 would like to thank the friends and members of my family whose advice, assistance and encouragement have helped in the production of this book.

J.C.

Introduction

It is difficult for those who never knew British India to comprehend how their countrymen lived in that strangely alien part of the Empire. Much has been written about the history of the British in India but it is the everyday detail that is so fascinating to a later generation. These memoirs are a mosaic of first-hand experiences of the wife of an Indian Police Officer – personal details and light-hearted anecdotes which give an insight into the lives of an ordinary family and a typical community during the difficult final years of the Raj.

The years preceding Indian Independence in 1947 were turbulent ones. In a country ravaged by war, political unrest and natural disasters, life was problematical and hazardous. In rural areas in particular, one had to cope with primitive conditions and disease, critical shortages of food and medicine, dangerous animals and devastating climatic conditions. The young *memsahib* coped with remarkable equanimity in situations which would have been anathema to her counterparts in England. It was the custom for British children to be schooled abroad, but having suffered six years of extreme loneliness herself as a child by being sent abroad, she opted to teach her own children despite the difficulties and without resources. Her children led supremely happy lives, uncomplicated yet adventurous, with the devoted attention of gentle and loyal servants.

Police work was fraught with danger because Indians were greatly influenced by custom, superstition and religion. Officers frequently had to defuse conflicts between Hindus and Muslims or to deal with cases of ritual murder and sacrifice. During the annual Tour, officials were isolated among thousands of Indians in potentially dangerous situations. The Tour, regarded as one of the great institutions of the Raj, was the opportunity for a district officer to attend to the problems and needs of the rural people and to put a finger on the pulse of the district. Most Indians looked to the British for their basic needs and protection, and in return gave their loyalty and support. Generally, the villagers, who formed the vast majority of the population, were not influenced by the Congress Party's 'Quit India' movement which was causing unrest in the urban areas, and could not conceive that the British might leave. These memoirs show, in a way that a scholarly history could never do, the relationship between the British and the indigenous people and the mutual respect and goodwill that existed between them.

Rampur could be a town almost anywhere in India. Indeed, there are many towns of this name and the Rampur of this book is just a typical up-country station. The characters in this story are based on real people – though names have been changed – and they were representative of the wider community. The extraordinary and challenging life produced many colourful characters: eccentrics, die-hards and snobs. The strict hierarchy and protocol, social taboos and racial prejudices in the upper echelons of society are portrayed alongside the integrity and devotion to duty which characterized those in the Imperial Services. Recruited from English public schools and top universities, young officers and administrators would immediately take control of vast districts. The standards and responsibilities that were demanded of them were usually very great and took their toll. Some *memsahibs*, discontented with the loneliness, deprivation and oppressive heat on the plains, retreated for long periods to hill stations which acquired a reputation for a glamorous social life and adulterous liaisons. But contrary to the popular concept of indolent *memsahibs*, most Englishwomen of that time made great sacrifices and showed remarkable endurance, staunchly supporting their husbands and often carving out roles for themselves. In the words of Lord Curzon, Viceroy of India from 1899 to 1905, the British in India were 'the strength and greatness of England'.

Those years of British rule bear a proud record of service fittingly commemorated by a plaque in Westminister Abbey, during which India was endowed with great legacies. A small number of civil servants – only 1300 at the height of the Raj at the beginning of the twentieth century – united the vast sub-continent with a network of railways, roads, bridges and irrigation canals. They set up a sound infrastructure and established law and order. Numerous schools and universities were built with a Western system of education which brought vision and hope to millions; by 1939, there were over 370 colleges of higher education, attended by 145,000 Indians. The colleges became the natural power-base of the nationalist movement which, ironically, brought about the downfall of the British in India. Despite the growing unrest and the antagonism to the Raj during those final years, the Imperial Services continued to serve with honour to the end and did their utmost to bring the country to Independence in peace.

Although the lives of the British became inextricably interwoven with India and its people, the chasm between the cultures was too great to be bridged and the imperial retreat was inevitable. Now, fifty years after Independence, the tremendous contribution of the British has largely been forgotten. *The Garlands of Rampur* is a tribute to all those who loved and served India.

Jill Cartwright
1997

'The British did a great deal of good by teaching us what they did, because we took up the challenge, we became different people, we grew mentally, and we got the fundamentals of liberty, equality, fraternity, all those socialist values.'

Mrs. Aruna Asaf Ali
(Former Nationalist Leader in the 1940s)

'When freedom came, the British left us valuable legacies, which have come in very useful in ruling ourselves to some purpose.'

M.R. Masani
(General Secretary of Congress Socialist Party, 1934–1939)

Chapter I

Rampur

Ship me somewheres East of Suez,
  where the best is like the worst,
Where there aren't no Ten Commandments
  an' a man can raise a thirst

RUDYARD KIPLING 'Mandalay'

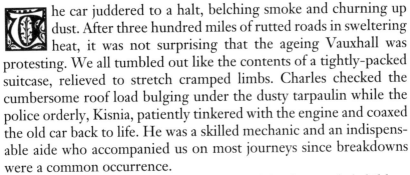he car juddered to a halt, belching smoke and churning up dust. After three hundred miles of rutted roads in sweltering heat, it was not surprising that the ageing Vauxhall was protesting. We all tumbled out like the contents of a tightly-packed suitcase, relieved to stretch cramped limbs. Charles checked the cumbersome roof load bulging under the dusty tarpaulin while the police orderly, Kisnia, patiently tinkered with the engine and coaxed the old car back to life. He was a skilled mechanic and an indispensable aide who accompanied us on most journeys since breakdowns were a common occurrence.

'We're nearly there,' Charles encouraged the disgruntled children crammed in the back with Ayah, Kisnia and the bearer, Hira Lal. Our two small dogs had found safe niches under the seats and the cat crouched resignedly in a wicker basket at my feet.

'Brenda, you mustn't delude yourself about Rampur,' Charles warned me. It's just another dreary up-country station. Fewer than fifty Europeans.'

Charles' promotion to District Superintendent that September of 1942 was his first independent charge after ten years in the Indian Police, and we felt exhilarated despite the intractable problems confronting us. The Congress Party's policy of non-cooperation and civil disobedience in the run-up to Independence was causing widespread unrest. The political disturbances added fuel to the endemic strife between Hindus and Muslims and it usually fell to the district officers to defuse or quell religious conflicts. The slightest provocation or infringement was enough to spark off a full-scale riot, especially during festivals and processions. Police officers tried to anticipate and forestall, or at least minimize, hostilities by positioning themselves near temples or along the route of a procession. But the chief concern of the district officers was the happiness of the ordinary man for whom political change had very little relevance and *Swaraj*[1] had no meaning.

We weaved our way through the bazaar, honking to alert the unwitting, for the arrival of a car was an unusual event in those parts. Ragged children, dogs and chickens scattered from their dusty playground. We drew up in the bustling market where sacred cows wandered freely among the open stalls, colourful with fruit and spices. We were soon surrounded by a curious mob, peering and reaching through the open windows. Alighting from the car, Charles greeted the crowds in Hindi and introduced himself for he needed to win the loyalty and support of the locals from the outset. They proceeded to relate the many and varied problems that beset them, for such an open hearing from the new Police-Sahib was too good an opportunity to miss.

'Sahib, this man is a *badmash!*[2] He is stealing my cow.'

'Hazur, I have many hungry mouths to feed . . .'

'*Baksheesh*, Sahib, *baksheesh*.'[3]

---

1 *Swaraj*: Home Rule.
2 *badmash*: rascal.
3 *Baksheesh*: money given as a gift or gratuity.

'*Ap mai ma-bap hai!*[1] Help me, Sahib!'

Charles' paternal role was quickly established and he assured his new charges that he had their interests at heart. Kisnia, who had no such tender feelings, severely reproved the crowd. 'Move! Let the Sahib pass!'

To the accompaniment of barking dogs and whining children, our bedraggled circus made its way to the civil lines where the small community of British families lived. The dak-bungalow,[2] where we were to spend our first few nights, was easily recognizable for it was much the same as those we had stayed in before. The thatched roof and mud-plastered walls peeped through a tangled mass of purple bougainvillaea. A haven for snakes, I thought uneasily. Recent rains had scored the bare compound into numerous furrows, softened here and there by nondescript shrubs and clumps of Canada weed.

With a new lease of life, the children and dogs rushed around excitedly on an exploratory tour while Ayah tried to keep some sort of control. 'The *Chota-sahib*[3] and missy-babas are very naughty,' she complained as she pursued them with their topees, for it was mid-afternoon and the heat was fierce. Phul Kumari was a gentle woman, dedicated to her charges but quite incapable of exercising any discipline over them.

'Give them a drink, Ayah, and watch them as well as you can,' I said comfortingly.

Leaving Hira Lal and Kisnia to prepare the rooms, Charles and I made our way to the bungalow opposite which was to be our new home. Like the archetypal up-country bungalow, it had high walls with gauzed skylights beneath a tiled roof and was surrounded by a wide verandah. Despite its peeling, whitewashed walls and unkempt garden, it seemed a veritable palace.

'Charles, it's wonderful!'

---

1 '*Ap mai ma-bap hai*': lit. 'You are my mother and my father.'
2 dak-bungalow: government rest house; sometimes referred to as a circuit house.
3 *chota-sahib*: junior sahib; the customary way of addressing the son of the Sahib.

The bungalow in Rampur. Despite its peeling walls and unkempt garden, it seemed a veritable palace.

The drawing-room of the bungalow.

He gave me a grateful smile. 'I hope you'll be happy here. I know you'll make the most of it.'

Henry Forsyth, the retiring officer who was a former colleague, was waiting on the verandah.

'Glad to see you, old boy.' Henry wrung Charles' hand. During the past two years he had grown thinner and his face was etched with weariness. The lonely life and heavy responsibilities had left their mark.

'You've lost weight, Henry,' I said tactfully.

'Shortages,' he said succinctly, patting his stomach. 'This is a cotton area. Sometimes difficult to get supplies.' We were soon to discover that this was a gross understatement for shortages during the war years became critical.

'When can you take over?' Henry asked eagerly.

'Straight away. We're staying at the circuit house for a few days until our things arrive.'

While the men settled down to business, I wandered round the almost empty bungalow, a larger version of those we had occupied previously. Gaunt square rooms with high ceilings, whitewashed walls and gaps for doorways offered little scope for originality. At least our cheap pieces of furniture, well-travelled veterans, would not look misplaced. Shafts of light from inaccessible skylights illuminated silvery webs and dancing dust particles. Geckos scuttled over the walls, frantically seeking cover, and upside-down bats lent comic interest. Fortunately, the hessian cloth that formed the ceilings restrained some of the less desirable inhabitants, which lived unmolested under the tiles and multiplied profusely. Not infrequently, snakes and scorpions found escape routes into the rooms below and sought new abodes in dark cupboards, drawers and shoes.

'Do you like what you see, Brenda?' enquired Henry with a grin.

'Well, it's home from home,' I answered cheerfully.

'By the way, since I'm going back to civilization, I'd like to get rid of some old bits and pieces. You may find them useful. Dirt cheap, of course. Bought 'em from a chap who got them from someone who . . . oh, you know how it is.'

'We'll take it all!' Charles and I said in one voice for we knew only too well how difficult it was to procure furniture, and much of ours would undoubtedly be reduced to its component parts during the rough journey.

'What about your pot plants, Henry?' I enquired eagerly, noticing lush palms and ferns nestling on the verandah. Pots substituted for flowerbeds since gardens were either sun-scorched and parched, or drowned by the monsoon torrents. Great efforts were made by some memsahibs to create gardens of pretty English annuals in the winter months but they were short-lived, devastated by the first blast of hot weather. The great thing was therefore pots, which were handed on with pride to the next incumbent.

'Good Heavens, you can have those,' said Henry. 'Hardly noticed them all this time. Must have come from my predecessor.'

The *mali*,[1] a wizened little Hindu with a goatee beard, came to introduce himself and offered a guided tour of the compound. 'I, Jagan, am watering these plants every day,' he announced expansively, pointing to the forest of verandah plants. Along the rain-scored path to the water tank, blackjacks and other rank growths flourished, gratefully responding to the watering from his leaking can. Flower beds defined by whitewashed rocks hosted healthy crops of weeds while ousted marigolds, those stalwarts of the most neglected garden, had taken root in the most improbable places. Shrubs of oleander, hibiscus and frangipani offered apologetic splashes of colour among the overgrown grass.

Jagan, anxious to impress his potential employer, led me to a clearing where *bhuta*,[2] pumpkin, brinjal and okra[3] grew in profusion. 'Memsahib will see that I am growing fine vegetables for the Sahib,' he explained proudly. Clearly, he spent the major part of his time cultivating them for his own family, for Henry could not possibly account for more than a small proportion of the crop. The *mali's* worried frown indicated that he could see difficult times ahead, for while sahibs could easily be fooled, memsahibs were quite a different matter.

'You can grow enough vegetables for all of us, Mali,' I said, 'provided you also work hard in the rest of the garden.' I spoke in Hindi for it was generally acknowledged that any worthwhile memsahib should speak in the vernacular.

'*Ap mai ma-bap hai!*' he exclaimed gratefully. '*Aré!* Poor man that I am, with many hungry mouths to feed!'

The parental role which was assumed of employers made one feel very responsible for the needs and wants of one's servants. It was necessary to be firm, but fair, and in return one received the most devoted service.

---

1 *mali*: gardener.
2 *bhuta*: Indian corn; maize.
3 okra: commonly known as lady's fingers. A finger-shaped vegetable with slimy flesh, which grows prolifically in tropical conditions.

The ayah, Phul Kumari, and Michael.

Scratching his head thoughtfully, the *mali* added, 'If Memsahib provides seeds of beanj-eanj, lettis-ettis and *bhuta*, in short time we will all have peace and plenty.' It was certainly a comforting philosophy, though one I did not share, and I nodded approvingly. Jagan, his job assured, salaamed deeply.

It was a couple of hours since the children had disappeared and I was wondering uncomfortably whether Ayah had managed to keep track of them. Suddenly Michael rushed up, flushed and excited, brandishing a large stick. He was followed by a breathless and tearful Ayah clutching the protesting girls by their hands. The children were giving poor Ayah a hard time, I thought guiltily, but at least they had their topees on.

'Mum, there's a disused well in the corner of the compound,' Michael informed me.

'Goodness! I hope you didn't go too close.'

'It's all right. It's full of rocks.'

'It's got cobras in it!' Susan announced dramatically. 'But don't worry, Mummy. Michael says he can kill them.' Susan, who trusted implicitly in her six-year-old brother, looked at him in open admiration.

'We tried to make them come out, but they wouldn't,' added Judy importantly.

'Really, Michael! Don't you realize how dangerous cobras are? Ayah, why didn't you keep them away from the well?' Clearly the children had had the upper hand.

'*Arébaprébap*, Memsahib!' she cried plaintively. 'I told them not to disturb the snakes but they would not listen. They are very wicked children, especially Michael-baba.' Ayah's voice rose to an hysterical wail as her pent-up grievances spilled out. 'This is indeed a dreadful place. There is no rice. These people are like animals for they eat only *jawar*.[1] Does Memsahib think I should eat *cotton*? For to eat *jawar* is surely to die!'

'I will make sure you get rice to eat, Ayah,' I assured her gently, 'and please tell me if there is anything else you need. Now go and have a rest in your quarters.'

'If Memsahib will give me permission, I will return to my own home where I can live and die in peace . . .'

---

1 *jawar*: a bitter grain, used as a substitute for rice.

Phul Kumari had been with us since Michael was two months old and had accompanied us on many transfers. She had been waiting for us by arrangement after Home leave when our ship – the *Viceroy of India*, which was later sunk by enemy action off the coast of North Africa – had docked at Bombay. A native of Chattisgarh, Orissa, she had the typical negroid features of her race with a round face, dark skin and long black hair which hung in a thick plait under her sari. I had become used to her despairing moans when the children were difficult and was always anxious to placate her for she was much-loved by us all.

'Why is Ayah so upset?' I asked Michael sternly after she had departed.

Michael was scornful. 'She was scared. I gave her a stick and told her to beat the cobras when they came out of the well.'

'That's very dangerous, Michael! What happened?'

'Nothing. Ayah just grabbed the girls and ran away. The cobras didn't even come out. She's just a coward.'

'Your're very lucky they didn't come out. Ayah was quite right to take the girls away. Don't go near that well again!'

'Don't you *want* me to kill those cobras?' asked Michael incredulously. 'They could *bite* the girls.'

'Well, that's true. Thank you, Michael, but we'll attend to the cobras some other time, perhaps . . . It's going to be fun living here, isn't it?' I said, without conviction.

The arrival of our possessions was heralded by a sudden downpour which turned out to be the grand finale of the rainy season. As the labourers skilfully negotiated the slippery morass, the furniture, which was already scarred and battered by numerous moves, became spattered with mud. We unpacked the crates of breakables with the mixed feelings of hope and dread which one experiences whilst awaiting the outcome of a delicate operation. Each loss was deeply mourned and survivors were welcomed back with extreme joy to be cherished even more.

The long rough journey by train and bus had taken its toll and there were numerous casualties among the more fragile items. 'Very sorry, this vase is broken, Memsahib.' Hira Lal apologetically produced several pieces of my precious crystal vase, a treasured wedding present. The bearer took a proprietary interest in all our household effects and seemed genuinely upset.

'Oh well, there'll probably be no flowers to put in it anyway,' I sighed, trying to be realistic.

'But *none* of this crockery's broken, Mum!' Michael was elated and triumphant for he had helped to pack the coarse utilitarian camp crockery. Over the years the battle-scarred veterans had resisted the roughest treatment and returned for more punishment.

The girls, who had been splashing excitedly in the puddles and slithering along the cement corridors, were tired and dirty. 'Is there any hot water for the children to bath?' I asked Hira Lal. Water was heated over a wood fire and carried to the *gussal-khana*[1] in four-gallon kerosene tins slung across a pole.

'Yes, Memsahib, but the bath tub is dented and leaking.' Fortunately we had taken over Henry's smaller hip-bath so the crisis was temporarily averted. It meant sitting with one's knees up to one's chin, but at least it would waste less water during the dry season.

'Please check the *gussal-khana* and the other things, Hira Lal,' I said. The bathroom was checked carefully before use as it was a favourite resting place for snakes and scorpions which entered by a large hole in the wall used for draining bath water. Not infrequently, a snake was coiled up in the tub or the chamber-pot, though fortunately the ungainly wooden commode towering grimly in the corner was protected by a hinged lid.

'There are no snakes, Memsahib,' Hira Lal reported back, and added solemnly, 'The piss-pot is cracked but the thunderbox is in working order!'

A carpenter was summoned from the bazaar to repair the damaged furniture. He was ushered unceremoniously to the drawing-

---

1   *gussal-khana*: bathroom.

room for audience with Hira Lal and myself. Removing his sandals in the doorway, the Mohammedan shuffled in nervously under the stern gaze of the bearer who, as a Hindu in the elevated service of the Police-Sahib, was an awesome figure.

'Speak, and do not waste Memsahib's time!' ordered Hira Lal.

The carpenter salaamed deeply. '*Aih-hai!* The furniture of the Memsahib is badly damaged. Two chairs are needing repair and the dining-room table is having three broken legs—'

'That is not so,' Hira Lal intervened belligerently. 'Only one leg of the table is broken.'

'Two other legs are breaking, Memsahib,' explained the carpenter defensively.

'Please check them, Hira Lal,' I said. It was quite likely that the carpenter was right, for on previous house-moves scarcely a leg from table or chair was undamaged. But it was necessary for the *khansama*[1] to assert his authority over the carpenter.

After a cursory check in the adjacent dining-room, Hira Lal confirmed that only one table-leg needed repair. 'But two others can be repaired some other time,' he added ambiguously.

'All right,' I agreed, restraining a smile. 'What else is broken?'

The little Mohammedan glanced nervously at the bearer. 'Memsahib's dressing-table is needing a new support for the mirror.'

Hira Lal interposed quickly. 'I will check. He is not to be trusted, Memsahib!' Clearly there was a score to be settled between the Hindu and the Muslim and the carpentry was incidental. Eventually Hira Lal grudgingly admitted that the repair was necessary. 'But there is nothing else!' he concluded firmly.

'How much do you want for this work?' I was anxious to end the tedious wrangle.

The carpenter closed his eyes and contemplated the complex mathematical problem. Substantial rake-offs would have to be paid

---

1 *khansama*: head servant/caretaker, who might also be the bearer or personal valet.

to Hira Lal, to the shopkeeper whose backyard he rented, to the police orderly who had introduced him, and so on. I knew that the carpenter would ask a fee much higher than he expected to receive, for no deal in India is complete without bargaining.

'All, all will cost only fifty rupees,' he said at length. 'Together with the furniture for the *nokar-log*.'[1] He glanced slyly at the bearer.

'Which furniture, Hira Lal?' I asked, puzzled.

It was understood that, as head servant, he was entitled to his *dastur*.[2] 'Just my *charpoy*[3] and my wooden box.' Like most Indian servants, Hira Lal was scrupulously honest and I trusted him implicitly. But the *dastur* was quite another matter; it could apparently be added to with impunity.

'And your table and your chair,' put in the carpenter smugly, realizing that the bearer had exceeded his perquisite.

'This man is exaggerating!' Hira Lal gave him a baleful look but the Mohammedan shrugged, knowing that he had scored his point.

Aspiring employees went to great lengths to get references and sometimes paid professional letter-writers for rigged testimonials. Occasionally, an employer wrote an ambiguous reference for an outgoing servant of dubious character or ability to warn other prospective employers. Some such letters became almost legendary, as for example, the following one:

> Ram Lal has been in my service for three long years during which he has served me to his complete satisfaction. Far from being heavy-handed like many servants, I have found him to be very light-fingered. I shall be considerably the poorer for his leaving. There is little doubt that he will do well with you.
>
> J. S. Roberts.

---

1 *nokar-log*: servants.
2 *dastur*: legal perk.
3 *charpoy*: bed, usually a wooden frame and rope webbing.

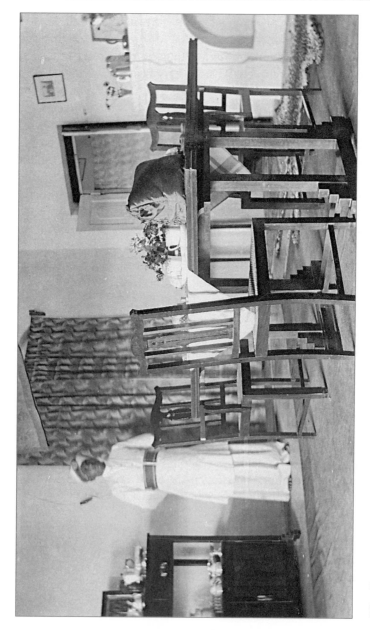

The dining-room and the bearer on duty.

Mohammed Ali's credentials as a cook were generally good, though one employer had stated ambiguously, 'He has done for me for several years. In fact, he almost did for me altogether.' But in the absence of other contenders for the job, we were prepared to overlook any lapses, at least to start with. He soon proved his worth, producing culinary wonders, despite shortages, with a primitive mud-brick *chula*[1] and poor facilities. It was not customary for memsahibs to intrude into the *bobajee-khana*[2] which was usually a separate hut at the back of the bungalow. It was the stronghold of the servants with the *bobajee* in command.

It was the responsibility of the bearer or *khansama* to engage other servants, and Hira Lal made it plain that it was to him that they owed their positions. A *masalchee*[3] and a *mehtar*[4] were recruited, each having his specific jobs. It was inconceivable that the *khansama* should wash the dishes or the *masalchee* sweep the floor. A domestic hierarchy based on religion and caste was quickly established among the servants. The bearer was like a major-domo, supervising and checking that all duties were properly discharged. Above all, he guarded his employer's interests, not permitting the least infringement; only he, the head of the household, was entitled to a *dastur*.

Each morning after breakfast the cook came to the drawing-room with his account book. We discoursed in time-honoured fashion while the dignified bearer hovered in the background, carefully monitoring proceedings, for a mere *bobajee*, and a Mohammedan at that, was not to be trusted. I resigned myself to the daily thrust and parry which was apparently necessary to retain status.

'Soup, Memsahib?,' asked Mohammed Ali. 'I can make brown soup and sippets.'

'Clear soup, thank you.' It didn't really matter because they both tasted the same, but at least one could see what was in the clear one.

---

1 *chula*: stove.
2 *bobajee-khana*: kitchen/cookhouse; *bobajee*: cook.
3 *masalchee*: cook's assistant; scullion.
4 *mehtar*: sweeper.

'But not too much water.' The cook would sometimes over-econ-
omize on soup, adding water to the pot day after day, long after the
bone had been sapped. 'Ask the *mali* for vegetables to add to the soup,'
I added, remembering the abundance which Jagan ostensibly provided for the Sahib's table.

He noted the ingredients in his account book and calculated aloud.
'One soup bone, four annas, six pies . . . *ghee*[1] for frying sippets, six
annas, two pies . . . about one rupee.'[2]

'That's too much!' intervened Hira Lal, who had also been totting
up the account. It was acceptable that the cook should take his perk
when he did the shopping by adding a little extra, but this was
overdoing it.

Mohammed Ali disregarded the bearer and continued, 'What
about curry-rice today, Memsahib? Served with *dhal*?'[3] Naturally, he
made superb curry despite the poor quality meat and was always quick
to suggest it. 'The recipe of my grandfather!' he said, grinning
broadly.

'We'd like a change if possible, Cook.'

'Some fish-fry then, Memsahib?'

'The fish from the bazaar is usually not fresh.'

'Perhaps a nice roast, Memsahib?'

'Yes, we'll have a roast,' I said resignedly. It was likely to be tough
goat or stringy chicken for little else was available. Beef was unobtainable since the killing of cows was offensive to Hindus. Meat was
always tough as it had to be eaten immediately after slaughtering.

'With sweet potatoes and lady's fingers?'

'Not lady's fingers. Any other vegetables, but *not* lady's fingers.'
Charles had an almost pathological dislike of the slimy vegetables
which grew in profusion.

'Surely you know that Sahib dislikes lady's fingers!' the bearer
reprimanded sharply.

---

1   *ghee*: clarified butter for cooking.
2   12 pies = 1 anna; 16 annas = 1 rupee (13 rupees = £1 in the early 1940s).
3   *dhal* (dal): a sauce made from lentils, often eaten with curry.

Unruffled, the cook continued, 'Meent sarce with goat?'

'Have you got mint?' I asked curiously, for there was none in the garden. Any refinement which could tenderize or disguise the goat would be welcome.

'*Gee haan*, Memsahib,' he said proudly, untying a knot in a *jharan*[1] to expose the tortured remains of the delicate herb whose sweet fragrance was overpowered by the grubby cloth.

'The meent is not fresh,' the bearer said angrily. For once, I welcomed Hira Lal's reproachful intervention.

'Is there anything else we need?' I asked quickly.

'Rice, Memsahib. One seer[2] rice, six annas—'

'You can get cheaper rice,' interposed the bearer.

'But only the best is good enough for Memsahib!' countered the cook slyly. 'The cheap rice has stones and weevils.'

Hira Lal was momentarily nonplussed. Taking advantage of his brief victory, the cook quickly proceeded to a discussion of desserts. They were not his forte and the bearer usually objected to his suggestions.

'Apricocks and custard bake?'

'Is there anything else?'

'Estewed pigs and custard.'

'We've had figs for the last three days, Cook.'

'Cornflour mouldy, then, Memsahib?' he suggested doubtfully. This was always the last choice, a tasteless dessert that looked like office glue and was difficult to improve or disguise; but it was good for the children.

'All right,' I assented, and concluded the battle of wits with a sigh of relief.

---

1 *jharan*: dusting cloth.
2 seer: approximately one kilogram.

Chapter II

One Great Family

English men and women in India are, as it were, members of one great family, alien under one sky.

MAUD DIVER *The Englishwoman in India* (1909)

'eetee Memsahib!'[1] announced Kisnia formally from his vantage point on the verandah. The next moment Dorothy Jameson bounded unceremoniously into the drawing-room where I was kneeling among packing-cases and crockery.

'So you're Brenda!' she boomed above Kim's hysterical barking. I rose unsteadily, plucking straw from my hair, but she restrained me with a heavy hand on my shoulder. 'No, don't get up. I just came to introduce myself and to help.'

'Pleased to meet you. Sorry about the mess.'

'Oh, don't worry about that. I can make myself at home anywhere.' Dorothy's large frame seemed to fill the room. As she looked around for somewhere to settle, I wondered if she had already forgotten her offer of help. She perched somewhat unwisely on a wooden crate

---

1 'Beetee': lit. BT (Bengal Timber Trading Company). Indians customarily refer to Europeans by their occupations, and a man's wife would be known by her husband's job.

studded with outsize nails that would have gladdened the heart of a *sadhu*,[1] while I continued to unpack.

'Nice to have another woman around the place. It's so dull with the same old faces day after day. What on earth possessed you to come *here* of all places? I suppose you had no choice.'

'Actually, it's promotion for Charles and we're looking forward to it.'

'Well, good luck to you,' she said with an effort. 'It's fine for Charles. He'll be busy and he'll get around like Tom does. *You're* the one who'll get bored. There's *nothing* to do here except read and play mah-jong or go to the Club.'

The Club, the social and sporting hub of all civil and military stations, could easily become an insidious part of one's life: a place to drink, a fertile ground for gossip, somewhere to while away hours at bridge, mah-jong, billiards or tennis.

Dorothy was clearly one of those memsahibs who had never adapted to the Indian way of life. I learned later that when she was eighteen, she had come out to India as part of the Fishing Fleet[2] on a P & O liner. Her wealthy parents had great aspirations of her finding a husband in the Indian Civil Service, regarded as the most elite of the British services. They were not altogether disappointed, for during the 'season' in Calcutta she enjoyed a tremendous social whirl and succeeded in catching the unwary and gentlemanly Tom Jameson of the Bengal Timber Trading Company. Although a well-respected company, BTT did not command the deference shown to the Imperial Services. To the Cheltenham girl, with all the refine-ments and pretensions of English nobility, this became a thorn which festered over the years.

Dorothy had soon found India a completely alien land. When she arrived at her bridal home, a simple up-country bungalow, she was completely disconcerted and shocked by the primitive and unattrac-

---

1 *sadhu*: a holy man or ascetic. He sometimes inflicts self-torture (such as lying on a bed of nails) to practise self-control.
2 Fishing Fleet: girls who came out to India in search of husbands.

tive conditions. The tales she had heard about snakes and tigers, malaria and dysentery, poverty and squalor, blistering heat and torrential rain soon became only too real. The romance and glamour of the East that she had dreamed of, did not exist.

In the course of his work as Branch Manager of BTT, her husband travelled widely, especially during the touring season, and she was left alone for days. She could not communicate with the servants, nor did she attempt to learn their language as any worthwhile memsahib would do. Her days were long and indolent for she left everything to her servants. Moving on every year or two to another small isolated station gave her no permanence or security and little opportunity to form friendships. Dorothy depended almost solely on her husband for company until the birth of her twin daughters, who brought a happy diversion for a few years. Then came the dreaded time when they had to be sent to England to be educated. After ten years of painful separations, eased occasionally by short spells of Home leave, the girls returned as virtual strangers.

Now, twenty years later with her children flown, she was disgruntled and bored. Separation and loneliness were part of the price the British paid for living in India. For the memsahib, this could be ameliorated not only by involvement in her husband's interests, but by finding a role for herself. Dorothy had clearly never done either. She had not accepted the challenge of India.

She was one of the unfortunate victims of the Raj, I realized, as she grumbled on about boredom and the discomforts of life. I was determined not to become like her. I would involve myself fully in my husband's work and in the day-to-day concerns of the household. I loved accompanying Charles on his tours of the district, rough and problematic though they were.

'I'm sure I won't get bored with the children around, and of course I'll go on tour with Charles,' I said cheerfully.

'*You* on tour?' She was incredulous.

'Of course. We both love riding and the children think camping is great fun.'

'Good Heavens! But it's so hot and dusty and primitive. And aren't you frightened of snakes and animals?'

It seemed pointless to respond. Instead, I said conversationally, 'It's good to see Jane and Alan Carstairs again. We've known them for years. And we met the Singhs yesterday. They're very nice people, aren't they?'

'Snobs, if you ask me! And Monique's so affected with her silly French accent. She's always saying "Pardon?" and "What means zat?" And as for those saris! Why doesn't she wear a proper dress?'

'But I think a sari suits her. She's very elegant and charming.' I felt for Monique, trying to adapt to a foreign way of life and struggling to learn not only English but also her husband's native language. She and Jashwant Singh, a courteous and cultured Hindu, had met when they were students at the Sorbonne. As the Deputy Commissioner of Rampur, Jashwant was well-liked and respected.

Dorothy's strident voice interrupted my thoughts. 'Have you met Horace and Marie Simpson?'

'Just briefly,' I said guardedly.

'You're lucky it was brief. Marie *never* stops talking except when she's eating.'

I giggled as I imagined Dorothy and Marie together – two large harridans with insatiable appetites competing for food and words. Encouraged by my amusement, she continually gaily, 'They've actually *retired* in Rampur. Tom says they must be *crazy*. How on earth can anyone in their senses *choose* to live here for ever? If I were in their shoes, we would go straight Home.'

A pictorial calendar left by Henry hung crookedly on a nail. She gazed nostalgically at the scene in which a cold lonely robin looked hopelessly at a bleak, frozen world. With a deep sigh she said plaintively, 'I hate this heat and the isolation. It's bearable if you can get away regularly, but of course we can't afford it. Eli and Rita Demetrios are always dashing off to Calcutta or going overseas. He works for Raleigh Brothers, you see, and has plenty of money. Damn *box-wallah!*[1] Life would be wonderful if we could get away now and again . . . buy some decent clothes and have some fun . . . I *love* going to Calcutta . . . dressing up and dancing . . . ' She patted imaginary curls into place with plump fingers, and for a few pleasant moments was lost in reverie, presumably visualizing herself fashionable and desirable at the Saturday Club in Calcutta where she had first met Tom.

'You must insist on your rights from the beginning, Brenda, or Charles will become like the rest of them. Men don't realize how hard it is for women here . . . how lonely it can be . . . You don't want to end up like Carrie Wood, do you? Mind you, with a husband like Fred, who can blame her? By the way, are you a member of the WVS?'[2]

'Yes, of course. Why?'

'Well the old battleaxe will be on to you in no time. Especially if you're the keen, intelligent type.'

'Well, I'm not, I'm afraid. But we must all do our bit.'

A welcome diversion was provided by Hira Lal's arrival with refreshments. 'A cup of tea, Dorothy? Or something else?'

Her eyes lit up eagerly. 'Well, my dear, since you *insist*, I'll have just a teeny-weeny gin. I find that tea fills me up so that I can't eat lunch.'

'Do help yourself,' I invited with all the graciousness I could muster.

Dorothy needed no urging and sprang with surprising agility from the packing-case to pour herself a neat gin. Clambering back on the crate she emitted an eloquent string of expletives and I looked up in surprise.

'Are you all right?'

'A bloody nail—' She rubbed her plump thigh vigorously and continued undeterred, 'Not that there's much to eat anyway. Tough

---

1 *box-wallah*: a derogatory term for a businessman, who ranked lowest in the professional and social hierarchy of the British in India. The prosperity of businessmen sometimes caused aggravation and jealousy amongst those in other services. Originally the term was applied to Indian traders who travelled up-country with goods in trunks or boxes.

2 WVS: Women's Voluntary Service.

old goat, or stringy chicken, or buffalo that's died of natural causes. Marie, Two-Ton-Tessie, always gets the best meat at the bazaar. Her cook's *always* first down there, snapping up the choicest bits.'

'Are there any tinned provisions available?' I enquired.

'Are you joking? We haven't seen anything in a tin for years except corned beef or K-rations which troops throw from the train. You might be able to buy some from beggars or your sweeper. The last tin of Poulson's butter that I bought was so oily that Tom wanted to use it for the car. It's a real miracle the way he keeps our old Plymouth going. He's very mechanically-minded,' she said proudly, 'and spends hours in his workshop so I hardly see him when he's at home.' A quiet, unassuming man whose opinions did not hold sway in his own home, Tom clearly sought refuge in his workshop.

Three gins later, a melancholy Dorothy made her way unsteadily to the car, promising to return shortly to fill in the gaps in her family history. 'You really should have let me help you, Brenda,' she chided. 'That's what I came to do, as you know.'

Charles, walking back from the *kotwali*,[1] had to leap for safety as Dorothy made a rapid take-off and skidded down the muddy drive. 'Silly woman!' he remonstrated. 'I've a good mind to arrest her for being drunk and disorderly!'

Another of the 'big happy family' as Dorothy referred to the local community, arrived a few days later. Carrie Wood cycled up the drive, skilfully negotiating the obstacles and ruts. Kisnia, his turban hanging from a branch, was idly conversing with another police orderly and was taken by surprise. A stickler for convention, he was annoyed at being caught off-guard, especially by this strangely masculine memsahib on a bicycle, with cropped hair and wearing uniform like a *Kaptaan Sahib*.[2] Kisnia's disapproval was obvious; nevertheless, he stood rigidly to attention, bare-headed – for there had been no

---

1 *kotwali*: police headquarters.
2 *Kaptaan Sahib*: captain; commanding officer.

time to retrieve his turban from the tree – and salaamed as Carrie leapt off her bicycle and strode into the drawing-room.

Caught unawares amidst a pile of books on the floor, I found my hand crushed in a powerful grasp. 'How do you do? I'm Carrie Wood, president of the WVS. Sorry we missed you the other evening.' In her grey uniform with highly polished buttons and badges, she looked businesslike and commanding.

I blushed as I recalled how Charles and I had retreated hastily after depositing our visiting card in the box outside their bungalow, relieved that our duty call had been accomplished so easily. Flexing my numbed fingers, I muttered, 'It's very kind of you to call round so soon.'

Carrie subsided into an armchair and lit a cigarette with an expert flick. 'Fred's on tour at present. Should be back in a week or two.'

'It must be very lonely for you. When Charles is away, I count the days till he returns.'

'Lonely? Good gracious, no. Far too much to do. Besides, Fred prefers to be on his own. I must say, I'm so glad you've come. I've been battling to stimulate interest in the Hospitality Committee. We're very short of keen, intelligent women.'

'Well, naturally, I'll do what I can to help.' I remembered Dorothy's warning, yet I felt flattered and I warmed to her.

'I understand that you're already a member of the WVS. Can you knit? The troops will soon be needing socks and balaclavas for winter.'

'Er . . . I'm not very good,' I said apologetically. She looked at me sternly and I added quickly, 'But of course I'll try.'

'You have uniforms, I take it?'

'Yes.'

'Well, if you need new ones, *dousuti*[1] can be bought at Deepchands and made up by the *derzi*.[2] I can let you have badges and buttons.'

---

1 *dousuti*: hard-wearing grey cotton drill, used for making uniforms.
2 *derzi*: tailor.

She consulted her notebook. 'There's a committee meeting next Monday at ten o'clock sharp. Please don't be late.'

Conversation flagged, but providentially, Hira Lal brought in the tea. He must have been aware of her rank for he was using the silver service and the best china tea set. He looked disapprovingly at the cigarette stubs and spilt ash beside Carrie's chair and replaced the small china ashtray with a large wooden one.

'Tea . . . er . . . Carrie?' I offered tentatively, wondering if I was crossing the bounds of familiarity with a senior officer.

'Thank you . . . er . . . Brenda,' Carrie replied with a thin smile. To my relief she waved away the plate of biscuits without looking at them. Dorothy had accounted for all the custard creams a few days before and only plain marie biscuits remained.

She crushed the stub of her cigarette into the *dhurri*[1] under the heel of her sensible shoe. I wished I had the courage to show my distaste; instead I enquired politely, 'What exactly does the Hospitality Committee do?'

'Well, obviously, we try to make the troops comfortable and welcome.'

Recalling Dorothy's words I said boldly, 'I mean, there's not much to do in Rampur, is there? When the troops come here they must be bored stiff with no cinema or night life. And the food in the barracks and troopships is probably better than we can provide.'

The police orderly, Kisnia

---

1 *dhurri*: coarse cotton rug.

Carrie lit another cigarette and surveyed me disdainfully through a series of smoke rings. I felt as though I were back at school, the foolish new girl being appraised by a haughty prefect. 'We've always found our guests overwhelmingly grateful,' she retorted coldly. 'And, of course, most people use their ingenuity to make interesting meals . . . the troops prefer *anything* to bully beef and tinned fruit.'

'Yes, of course,' I muttered, fighting the desire to say I'd give a lot for some iron rations. I was annoyed with myself for feeling intimidated. The warmth I had initially felt for her was evaporating. Presumably my intelligence rating had diminished too.

'See you at ten o'clock on Monday,' she reminded me firmly as she rose to leave, and I resisted the urge to salute. She paused incautiously to pat Kim's head but our terrier, having no respect for rank, growled forbiddingly and bared his teeth. This time Kisnia was prepared – having retrieved his turban from the tree – and held out her cycle in readiness. Mannishly, Carrie mounted and pedalled off down the drive, without a wave or backward glance.

'Who the hell was that?' asked Charles uncivilly, emerging from his study.

'That, I'd have you know, is my superior officer. I've been assessed and found wanting. Carrie Wood, no less.'

'Poor old *Lukri!*[1] Henry warned me to give her a wide berth.'

'It's all very well for you cowering among your dusty files but I can't avoid her. She's on the track of all keen, intelligent women!'

Charles laughed heartily. 'Oh well, in that case you should be safe!'

'Did you know that the Pintos have retired in Rampur?' I asked Charles. 'It must be four years since we saw them. Let's invite them to tea.'

'Good idea. How many children do they have?'

---

1 *Lukri*, which means 'wood' in Hindi, is a common nickname for people of that name.

'Eight, I think. The older ones are quite grown-up now, so I don't expect they'll come.'

Mrs Pinto, a large homely woman, took great pride in her big family and ruled them with firm but benevolent authority. Neighbourly and kind, she would appear at times of need laden with sweetmeats, chutneys and other delectable home-made goods. I recalled with gratitude how she had helped to nurse Michael when he had been seriously ill with bronchitis.

Many years of service in the police had instilled in Mr Pinto a strict discipline which he imposed on his family. Their horse-drawn tonga arrived exactly on the hour. He marshalled his children into line and led them sedately up the drive. Uniformly dressed as if for a school excursion, the boys wore khaki shorts and shirts and the girls wore frilly pink frocks. Mrs Pinto, with a white solar topee and incessantly waving fan, clucked instructions to her brood from the rear.

'*Chota Sahib, Chota Memsahib aur baba-log!*'[1] announced Kisnia. *Chota*[2] on this occasion denoted rank rather than size, for Mr Pinto had worked as Reserve Inspector under Charles at a previous station. Mrs Pinto had grown even larger since I had last seen her and each step was an effort.

After prolonged greetings we settled down to tea on the verandah where a light breeze alleviated the oppressive heat. 'My, this is just like old times,' remarked Mrs Pinto happily in the nasal sing-song voice characteristic of Eurasians. 'Where are the *butchas*?'[3] My children had an embarrassing habit of disappearing when other children arrived to play with them. They were probably peeping from bushes or corners, assessing the strangers.

'They'll come along at any moment,' I lied.

'And how are you, Missus? You and your hubby going on fine, I hope and pray.'

---

1 *baba-log*: children.
2 *chota*: small.
3 *butchas*: babies or small children.

In response to my enquiries, she said, 'We are oll-right. Onlee I have to be veree careful with my angina. You know how?' 'Yes, of course,' I sympathized. Mrs Pinto spoke of her heart disease like an old friend since she had lived with it for years and could always depend on it as a topic of conversation.

After an exhaustive discussion on angina, I enquired about her eldest daughter, Patsy. Mrs Pinto raised her hands in despair. 'Oh my, we have had such a time with that one. One thing after another it is. First she is falling and spraining her ankle, then she is going down with dysentery and we are having to call Dr Pradhan. Now she is wanting to be a *nun* of all things. I tell you, I am going nearly mad!' She breathed heavily as she considered the problem, her fan working overtime. Runnels of perspiration streamed like tributaries through the pink powder on her face.

'Perhaps it's a religious phase,' I suggested tactfully.

'That is just what I am telling her but she is insisting, "Mummee, it is a vocation. I will pray for you when I am a nun and then you will be saved." But I am saying to her, "That is rubbish, Patsy. How can your prayers save us? Better to stay at home and do some work." '

Cissy unwisely came to her sister's rescue. 'But Mummee, you know that Patsee is veree holee. Mother Stanislaus is always telling her in school that she must become a nun.'

'Cissy, you are too bold! You must not talk out of turn.'

This emotive issue was clearly getting out of hand. Recalling that Jackie, her eldest son, had always been a submissive and biddable child, I asked after him.

'Oh, my Gawd, Missus, that Jackee!' Mrs Pinto remonstrated, crossing herself. 'He has a good job on the railway, but he is thinking onlee of parties and dancing. Night after night he is going dancing at the Institute at Bhusavel. Now, if you please, he is after some girl there and he is wanting to get married. But I am saying, "Jackee, you must first work hard and earn plentee of monee. It is not the time to get married. You are onlee a *butcha*." '

'What does you husband feel about it?'

'My hubby, he is simply mad with him. "I will beat that *chokra*[1] so hard that he will forget about getting married," he is saying. "And Patsee also. She will not be so holee then." ' But Mr Pinto, happily reminiscing with Charles, had temporarily forgotten the aberrations of his children.

Ivy was sitting with hanging head, awaiting her turn for censure. Of what sin could this sweet child be guilty? 'Another Vimto, Ivy?' I asked gently. She shook her head and gulped.

'Come, child, come. Don't be shy. Where are your manners?' admonished her mother. 'She is too shy, this one, especially with the boys.' Ivy blushed deeply, on the verge of tears, while her brothers and sisters giggled and shifted nervously.

Mrs Pinto caught sight of Michael who was peeping round a corner. He was presumably hoping for something to eat for it was unlikely that he had come to be sociable. 'Oh, my, how that child has grown. Just fancee! Don't be shy, Michael. Come to Auntee,' she invited.

'I'm *NOT* shy!'

'You see, Ivy, *he's* not shy.' But Michael edged away, deciding that a piece of cake was not worth the loss of freedom. Her entreaties were no more successful with Susan and Judy who glowered at her from a distance. 'Just like little angels, they are!' she cried rapturously.

Eventually, after firm intervention from their respective fathers, all the children went off to play together. As the hostile group disappeared, Mrs Pinto leaned forward and whispered conspiratorially, 'Now we can talk *properlee!*'

---

1 *chokra*: boy.

Chapter III

The Romantic East

I can never forget the intoxicating smell of incense or the aroma of spices in an Indian bazaar. Everywhere there is movement and colour and noise. Bullock carts, *gharries*,[1] rickshaws and bicycles seem to be in perpetual motion and the air is heavy with dust. Pi-dogs[2] slink around grabbing a morsel here and there, chickens run riot and sacred cows wander at will. As you stroll through the labyrinth of squalid stalls and mud-plastered huts, you side-step piles of dung. There is a continual buzz of flies; the juicy cut surfaces of melons and pumpkins are speckled black with them. Exotic fruit, sticky sweets and colourful spices are piled alongside foul-smelling *bummalo*,[3] soft silk saris draped incongruously over dirty bags of grain, and delicate handcrafts crammed among banal *dekshis*.[4] Little brass bells suspended from awnings jingle as you pass, their musical sound drowned by raucous shouts of vendors and loud bartering. Above the general cacophony is heard the plaintive strain of a sitar[5] and the monotonous drumming of the tabla[6] beating out the languid pace of India.

---

1 *gharries*: carts.
2 pi-dogs: ownerless dogs; pariah-dogs.
3 *bummalo*: 'Bombay duck', a small strong-smelling fish which is dried and salted.
4 *dekshis*: cooking pots.
5 sitar: Indian lute.
6 tabla: small twin drums.

Rampur Bazaar (1942).

You can expect almost anything in the confusion: an ash-smeared *sadhu*, cross-legged and immobile in prayer, an armless or legless beggar, or a festival dancer in a panther skin. You may stumble over a pavement sleeper bundled in a blanket or an urchin pounding chillis on a stone. You may even be confronted by a fearsome, beady-eyed cobra with extended hood, swaying to the high-pitched notes of a snake-charmer's pipe. The sights, sounds and smells of an Indian bazaar bombard the senses and leave you reeling.

The bazaar was the social hub of the Indian community, a meeting place where bartering was done and contracts made. Memsahibs were seldom seen at the bazaar and it was forbidden territory to European children. The cook in the European household did the shopping. He went daily to get the best bargains and make a little bit on the side – that was his *dastur*.

Rampur Club was built in the latter part of the nineteenth century when Rampur was a military cantonment[1] and a sizeable civil station. As with other district clubs, it was the focus of social life and sporting activities for army and civilian families. An officer who was not a member was usually regarded as either an outcast or a rebel. Subordinates, however, had to be seconded for the limited places available to non-officials, and those in 'inferior' occupations such as box-wallahs, technicians and railway workers, were generally black-balled.

In its heyday, Rampur Club's sporting facilities included a polo field and a cricket pitch. The extensive grounds had fallen into disuse but there was still a *murram*[2] tennis court and a crumbling clubhouse. Yellowing bridge tables continued to do duty for the undiscerning, but billiard enthusiasts had to admit defeat for 'a cloth untrue with a twisted cue'[3] defied the most skilful player. The most used amenity was undoubtedly the bar which was strictly a male preserve. A *burra-peg*[4] of whisky, diluted with soda and ice, was the great thirst-quencher. Women met on the verandah or in a lounge known as the *moorghi-khana*[5] to exchange trivia and sip *chota-pegs*, while children were supervised by their ayahs.

The small dusty library, enjoyed by an increasing population of white ants, included Victorian classics and historical tomes on the Indian Mutiny. Well-thumbed issues of *Blackwoods* and *Punch* provided light relief while tattered copies of the *Illustrated London News*, featuring the Empire Tour of the Duke and Duchess of York,[6] were still enjoyed by staunch royalists. For those wanting an escape from reality, 'modern' authors such as Maud Diver and Flora Annie Steel provided a glimpse into the Romantic East. Their enviable characters

---

1 cantonment: a permanent military base with lodging for troops.
2 *murram*: sandy soil.
3 W. S. Gilbert: *The Mikado*.
4 *burra-peg*: double tot (usually referred to whisky); *burra*: large.
5 *moorghi-khana*: hen-house.
6 Afterwards, King George VI and Queen Elizabeth).

enjoyed a glamorous social whirl alternating with terrifying adventures that always ended happily.

Although the Club had fallen on hard times, it was still the hub of the local society and a forum for gossip. On the cool verandah small groups lounged in cane chairs, sipping iced drinks and chatting. Children, with their ayahs in attendance, played in the dappled shade of a spreading goldmahore, taking turns on a crude swing.

'How lucky you are to have a good ayah, Brenda,' commented Rita. 'My old Sarifa spends her time sleeping. Eli thinks she's unwell.'

'She probably takes *bhang*,'[1] said Dorothy ominously. 'It's common, you know. They keep it under their little fingernails which they grow long specially for the purpose.'

'Heavens! I wonder if Sarifa takes it. I mean, what about my children?' Rita's voice held a note of hysteria.

'Well, we had a couple of nasty experiences when our girls were small. You can't be too careful, you know. They feed it to the children to keep them quiet. You don't notice anything at first—'

'*Dorothy!*' Tom, who had been listening uncomfortably in the background, reprimanded her sternly. 'Don't put the wind up her!'

But Dorothy was irretrievably launched and Tom's protest went unheard. Rita's curiosity was roused and she persisted anxiously. 'Was your ayah actually caught with it?'

'No. When they came to examine her, she had nothing. She'd probably got rid of it.'

'Oh God! Perhaps Sarifa should go. But how can I prove anything?'

Marie joined in with relish. 'You can always tell when someone's addicted because their pupils become dilated. And eventually an addict goes off his head or falls into a coma.'

Rita looked aghast. Oblivious of her anxiety, Dorothy continued her jeremiad. 'We had to dismiss our *masalchee* some years ago because he was an addict. He kept staring at me in such a peculiar way that I just didn't feel safe.'

---

1 *bhang*: Indian hemp (wild marijuana), used as a narcotic.

Marie turned on me aggressively. 'You don't seen to be at all concerned, Brenda.'

'Well, I think you've got this out of proportion,' I replied, recalling what Charles had said. 'Our children are exposed to so many dangers that we would be neurotic if we got worked up about everything.'

'How can you be so casual?'

'I'm not casual. I'm aware of the problem and watch for strange behaviour. I think a child is more likely to be bitten by a snake than have an overdose,' I added, remembering the occasion when Michael had unwittingly shared a chair with a krait, one of India's most deadly snakes, and the numerous times we had had close encounters with cobras.

'That's true,' agreed Rita, with a deep sigh of relief. 'Compared to other things, *bhang* is a minor problem. Think how easy it is to get malaria or cholera or typhoid.'

'Or break a limb . . .' I murmured, as I watched Susan sailing high on the crude swing. 'Susan's still suffering from rickets, you know – her bones are not very strong and that really *is* a worry. She's allergic to milk and I can't always get adequate substitutes.'[1] There was a poignant silence as I went to take her off the swing whose frayed ropes were in imminent danger of breaking.

The little church was a curious building like an outsize oval beehive with walls several feet thick. It had been built as an arsenal when Rampur had been an army headquarters in the previous century. One had to edge through a narrow entrance into the gloomy, airless interior where only a simple wooden cross indicated that it was a house of prayer. It stood aloof in a dusty acre, softened only by a few wilting marigolds.

The cemetery lay a couple of miles away on the outskirts of the town and was presided over by an elderly caretaker who, for the sum of ten rupees a month, attempted to keep the encroaching jungle at

---

1 Powdered milk substitutes lacked essential ingredients and required supplements like fresh orange juice which was often unobtainable.

bay. A huge banyan tree,[1] with a maze of branches stretching down like gigantic tentacles, dominated the area and provided a fine abode for snakes. Crumbling gravestones preserved some of the stirring history of a bygone age. The blood of many had been spilled in the Indian Mutiny and during skirmishes in the past century. Some adventurers had been savaged by wild animals and met violent deaths. Certain epitaphs caused speculation: Was it an inexpert pig-sticker or the victim of oppression in a hierarchical system who was 'driven to his end by a pig'? There was a 'victim of a serpent' and one who had 'found himself a safer place'. The fatalities of disease were numerous: typhoid, cholera, blackwater fever and dysentery had all taken their toll. Sudden death and suicide among the British were common in India. There were many large cemeteries for the British dead all over the country and they were out of all proportion to the sizes of the towns and military cantonments. Even the young and the stout succumbed to the rigours of life and to overly heavy responsibilities. Numerous graves of children and young people were a sombre warning of the fate that could overtake those who failed to adapt or take precautions. For many, presentiments of death would no doubt have been echoed by the words of Rupert Brooke:

> If I should die, think only this of me:
>   That there's some corner of a foreign field
> That is for ever England.

A church service with a visiting padre was quite an event. We were fortunate to have a church in Rampur as most outlying districts did not and services, if any, were held in private homes. When Judy had been christened, the dining-table covered with a white cloth had served as the altar.

In preparation for the service, I rummaged in my wardrobe for my only hat. It was a pink straw with a wide brim that drooped

---

1 banyan tree: the wild fig, sacred to Muslims and Hindus.

dejectedly. As I tried it on in front of the mirror, the girls watched in fascination.

Susan giggled. 'Mummy, why are you wearing that funny hat?'

'To go to church,' I explained, wondering uneasily whether the rest of the congregation would react like her.

'Can we go too?' chorused the girls.

'No, not this time. Next year, perhaps.'

'But Michael's going. It's not fair. He has all the fun.'

'We don't go to church to have fun,' I admonished. 'Besides, little girls who giggle would be turned out.'

Judy's face puckered. 'Even Ayah's going and she hasn't got a hat,' she sobbed.

'Please, Mummy! I promise not to laugh at your hat,' Susan begged.

Relenting, I impressed on the girls the due solemnity of the occasion. While I was wondering disconsolately how to revive my battered headgear, Hira Lal brought a chit[1] from Dorothy marked 'Urgent'.

'Dear Brenda,' she wrote, 'Can you lend me a hat for the service on Sunday? A rat has eaten a hole in mine and I've only got a topee. I've asked Jane, but she's lent her spare to Marie. Any old thing will do. Love, Dorothy.'

Perhaps the girls would find my hat less distasteful on Dorothy, I thought. Impulsively, with a sense of guilty relief, I dispatched it to her with a note of apology about its condition. I decided to go without a hat. But later an idea came to me. Monique was a Catholic so she would certainly not be attending the service. If she had any hats, they were sure to be *à la mode*. As it turned out, Monique had no fewer than four from which to choose. The fifth she had lent to Rita, she explained apologetically.

At the appointed time the small congregation including Ayah, who like many Indians had converted to Christianity, filed into the church. An assortment of restored headgear decorated the pews and my pink

---

1 chit: note (telephones were rare in smaller stations and messages were sent with servants).

straw looked relatively chic atop Dorothy's bouffant hair. Marie, with Jane's second best firmly secured with pins like meat skewers, led the hymns in a throaty contralto. Carrie had overcome the problem of a hat by wearing uniform.

Susan and Judy behaved with decorum, following the service with every appearance of interest and devotion. They gazed with awe at the padre in his unusual flowing robes as he addressed the congregation from the pulpit. The reverent silence that followed his blessing was shattered as Susan enquired shrilly, 'Mummy, is that God?' Judy added conversationally, 'He does talk a lot, doesn't He?'

A skilled *derzi* was in great demand and was booked for weeks in advance. Abdul Gaffar's reference was impressive: 'He can make old garments look like new, put patches on anything and make an exact copy of your neighbour's dress.' A small man with a goatee beard and cheerful grin, he ensconced himself in a corner of the verandah with his ancient Singer sewing machine. He sat cross-legged on a small mat with the tools of his trade carefully laid out beside him: scissors large enough to clip a hedge, a tape measure and an outsize pincushion like a silver-tipped hedgehog.

I amassed a daunting pile of linen and clothes in need of mending, some items threadbare and scarcely repairable. By evening the ragged pile had been miraculously converted into useable items: sheets, long since condemned, restored; the girls' outgrown dresses a size larger; and Michael's trousers decorated with diamond-patches, ready for further punishment.

The following day Abdul Gaffar produced a pattern for my new dress. 'This pattern will be very suitable for Memsahib,' he suggested, showing me a tattered illustration of a dress he had obviously made countless times. 'I have just made the same dresses for Beetee Memsahib and Simpson Memsahib.'

The thought of being dressed like a miniature of Dorothy and Marie prompted me to unearth one of my old patterns, albeit unfashionable. He studied it carefully and measured the material expertly between his nose and outstretched hand. He shook his head despondently. 'You will need half a yard more, Memsahib.'

'The material was bought in Bombay and I cannot get more. Please make smaller pleats so the skirt uses less material.'

'Box-pleats are looking just right on Memsahib,' he said, having sized up my inadequate vital statistics. 'They are looking very nice on Beetee Memsahib and Simpson Memsahib. I can make faithful copy.'

I had no desire to create the illusion of a fuller figure despite his obvious admiration for my neighbours' more ample proportions. 'I do not like box-pleats, Derzi,' I said firmly. 'And I do not want a dress the same as Beetee Memsahib and Simpson Memsahib.'

He shook his head sadly like one who had no option but to comply with a lost cause. 'As Memsahib wishes,' he said resignedly.

In the following weeks the hum of Abdul Gaffar's Singer became as much a part of our lives as the croaking of the monsoon toads, the whine of mosquitoes and the monotonous drumming of the tabla in the bazaar. His gondola-shaped shoes and white cloth cap were always nearby. Indeed, I never saw him without his 'Gandhi' cap, but his admiration for Gandhi ended with his cap for he was a devout Mohammedan. At certain times each day he could be seen at his devotions on his small prayer mat. Sometimes the children, inspired by his example or more probably fascinated by his antics and murmurings, would place the doormats alongside and join in. Undeterred, he continued his prayers with enviable single-mindedness.

During Abdul Gaffar's term of employment Mrs Pinto paid me an unexpected visit. I saw her familiar black umbrella bobbing up and down the drive, its long ferrule projecting above the bushes like a periscope. In her wake came two of her daughters and a *chokra* balancing a basket on his head. A lean mongrel rushed around investigating territorial rights while I restrained our hysterical dogs.

'Good morning, Missus. I've brought some fresh mango *kasoundi*[1] for you and sweeties for the *butchas*. Ivy! Gracie! Say good morning

---

1 *kasoundi*: a type of chutney.

nicelee.' Without giving them time to respond she continued, 'My, what girls these are! No manners at-oll!'

'Good morning, Missus,' chorused the two girls faintly.

'Go get the things from the *chokra*,' she ordered. The girls scuttled off gratefully followed by Spotty, the mongrel, with our dogs in pursuit.

Over a cup of tea we settled down to a detailed discussion of the many and varied problems besetting the Pinto family. A ray of hope brightened the gloom as Patsy had changed her mind about becoming a nun and had decided to take up dressmaking instead. This was a trade after her mother's own heart for Mrs Pinto was an expert seamstress.

'Thanks to Virgin Mary and Mother Stanislaus!' she exclaimed, crossing herself devoutly. 'Mother found out that Patsy was sending holee pictures to a boy at St Joseph's. And she was waving to the boys and being veree bold, so Mother is telling her that she has no vocation as a nun after-oll.' Mrs Pinto sighed with relief and mopped her forehead.

Carefully avoiding the usual topics of her angina and her husband's blood pressure, I asked after Jackie. Mrs Pinto's straw fan shuttled to and fro and her chair creaked protestingly as she wrestled with her emotions. I wondered whether the angina or blood pressure would have been safer topics after all.

'You don't understand, Missus, how it is,' she said at length. 'That girl he is after, Cissy Dacosta, her father is onlee a chargehand on the railway.' Leaning forward, she whispered conspiratorially, 'Besides, they are living just like natives!'

Fortunately, Abdul Gaffar's sewing machine whirred into action, vibrating like an aircraft about to take off, and provided a welcome diversion. Nodding in the direction of the *derzi*, Mrs Pinto said disapprovingly, 'You've got *that* chap here, eh?'

'Yes, I'm having a dress made up for myself, and some frocks and knickers for the girls,' I explained cautiously.

'And what, may I ask, is he charging?'

'Five rupees for my dress. And for the girls, three rupees for the frocks and twelve annas for the knickers.'

Mrs Pinto raised her hands in protest. '*Three rupees!* Oh my, Missus! That's too much. Why don't you cut him down? Just one-eight, no more. And onlee six annas for the knickers.'

To avoid argument, I promised to negotiate afresh with the *derzi* although I had already made up my mind to increase his humble fees.

The children and dogs had returned, and Kim and Spotty were circling around each other aggressively, taking turns to lift their legs against my cherished pot plants. I dared not look at Hira Lal standing nearby, aware of his disgust at the ill-mannered dog of a chota-sahib[1] taking such liberties.

'Spotee! Spotee! Oh my Gawd, that dog is awful! I don't know why he follows us all the time. We must push off quicklee.' The children were hastily summoned and issued with a flurry of instructions: 'Say goodbye nicelee. Put on your topees. Pull up your pettee, Gracie. Go call the *chokra*, Ivy.'

Mrs Pinto unfurled her umbrella and led the procession off at a brisk pace, cautioned by Ivy, 'Mummee, mind your angina!'

'I'm oll-right, child, just give me your arm.'

'*Hut!*'[2] said Hira Lal under his breath as the mongrel lingered to raise a leg. He was helped on his way by a well-aimed kick.

In the up-country districts one relied heavily on the post for communication. Newspapers, which came weekly on the mail train from Bombay, were read eagerly despite being out of date for they were our only source of news and opinion. Magazines from England, a month or more after publication, were nevertheless welcomed, read avidly and passed from hand to hand. Mail-orders became an integral part of our lives and many hours were spent perusing the Army and Navy Stores' catalogue.

---

1 chota-sahib: junior officer.
2 '*Hut!*': 'Get out!'

In the cool dry weather the travelling salesmen did their rounds. With a tin trunk called a Wood's box[1] strapped to his bicycle or perhaps with a retinue of coolies bearing trunks on their heads, the salesman would bring all manner of tempting goods. The articles were laid out on the verandah and friends would converge like bees round a honeypot. From the luxurious to the utilitarian, he had it all: Kashmiri shawls and silken underwear, baby clothes and embroidered cloths, celluloid dolls and safety pins. It required both restraint and bargaining power to procure one's requirements without overspending.

There was a succession of itinerant traders and entertainers, holy men and quasi-medics. A dentist was in great demand and would set up a makeshift dispensary in a hut for a few days. An expert at extraction, he would offer to remove several teeth for reduced rates. This caused a dilemma for some as there was no knowing when he would return. Fortunately, my family had sound teeth and our occasional visits to the cities sufficed for our dental needs. Self-styled oculists diagnosed visual defects of which you were previously unaware, and were eager to prescribe spectacles from an impressive range of bifocals, pince-nez and horn-rims.

Sadhus[2] and *fakirs*[3] who came soliciting alms were not to be denied. With their skinny, naked bodies daubed with saffron and ashes, their matted hair and their faces scored with curious markings, these sinister men were held in considerable awe by the locals. It was said that the mere possession of an article of clothing, or even a few strands of hair or fingernail parings, gave them mysterious power over the owner. It was far better to place a small offering in their begging bowls and avert the evil eye . . .

The itinerant showman with his troupe of performing animals was always welcome. Heralded by the monotonous clackety-clack of a

---

1 Wood's box: called after a certain Mrs Wood in Calcutta who conceived the idea of supplying useful household items to out-of-the-way places.
2 *sadhu*: a holy man, sage or ascetic (usually Hindu).
3 *fakir*: a holy mendicant or ascetic (usually Muslim).

Itinerant entertainer performing a 'tiger' dance.

small drum, he would set up stage on the bare ground with only the scrub or a *babul*[1] as a backdrop. An audience seemed to materialize

---

1   *babul*: thorn tree.

from nowhere, as is the way in India, and enthusiastically supported the productions. These varied little from year to year so the actors were well-drilled and apparently willing. Their lives depended on their performances as it was a relatively simple matter to find substitutes.

The first actors were usually a pair of vervet monkeys secured by leather thongs around their tiny waists. The endearing little maiden in colourful skirt and bonnet rejected the advances of her lover, dressed in tattered pants. Wrathfully he turned on her and belaboured her with a stick. Squealing pathetically, she took refuge behind the showman and would not respond to her suitor's entreaties. However, a little word in her ear from the trainer brought about a change of heart and the lovers' quarrel was resolved. Interest was added to the story by asides such as searching for fleas or squabbling over nuts and titbits thrown by appreciative onlookers. Finally, the happily reunited pair sat together on a stool while the drum sounded out the monkey version of the Wedding March.

The dancing black bear, a popular performer in every show, was controlled by a tethering rope attached to a ring through its sensitive nose. Its agitated prancing was merely an attempt to relieve the searing pain caused by the jerking of the rope. During a tour the helpless bear shambled after its tormentor for mile after mile, its suffering aggravated by the heat.

A more humane display was given by parakeets and pigeons which were obviously trained with great patience. A pigeon, harnessed between the traces of a tiny celluloid cart, was driven by two colourful parakeets. Spurred on by sharp pecks from the relentless drivers, the pigeon dutifully completed several circuits before flying off to receive a reward of grain from its trainer. In the second act a miniature cannon was charged with a small amount of 'gunpowder'. A tattered parakeet, the veteran of many performances, scampered up to light the fuse with a burning taper in its beak. Emerging triumphantly from the resulting explosion with smoke-blackened plumage, it claimed a bouquet of chillies and savoured the hot seeds with obvious delight.

Encouraged by this reward, the little bird had to be restrained from relighting the fuse.

Acrobats and stuntmen staged the most extraordinary and skilful shows with the simplest props. A young boy shinned up a fifteen-foot pole secured with guy ropes, and balanced horizontally on his navel using a shield the size of a large button. He pivoted round at dizzying speed and then dangled by his toes from a small crossbar with a nonchalance that would have awed the most daring trapeze artist. Far from being hushed into respectful silence, the audience applauded raucously and exhorted him to greater efforts. An astonishing and grotesque performance was given by an old man who lifted a boulder, too heavy to be raised by hand, with suckers attached to his eyes. Horrified by this masochistic act, Charles called out to him to stop. But apart from slightly bloodshot eyes, he had suffered no obvious ill-effects.

It was with some surprise that we received an invitation to tea from Francis le Grange, a recluse who lived in a ramshackle bungalow near the civil lines. Occasionally the eccentric old pukka-sahib[1] was seen in the bazaar where he sold produce from his smallholding. He sometimes called on Charles to discuss official matters.

'Don't ask too many questions,' cautioned Charles. 'He's a modest fellow and doesn't like talking about himself. He's had quite a distinguished career as an engineer and has overseen the construction of some very fine bridges.'

'He must be very lonely. Was he ever married?'

'His wife died about twenty years ago and he's lived alone ever since. But he seems quite content. He said something about living out his time here. There's nothing for him to go back to England for. Actually, I don't think he's very well, poor old chap.'

Francis welcomed us warmly and we admired his neat garden and well-kept vegetable patch. The drab lounge was strictly utilitarian,

1 pukka-sahib: gentleman.

without ornament or picture to give a personal touch. I had hoped that an *objet d'art* or a photograph would provide a subject of conversation.

'I've got rid of most my possessions,' Francis explained as if reading my thoughts. 'No point in hoarding things at this stage of my life.'

His bearer set out the tea and home-made scones on a long low table draped with a white cloth. Surprisingly friendly and relaxed, he talked about his youth in England and his travels in India during the course of his career. He volunteered little about his achievements but it was evident that he had served with distinction in the Imperial Services.

After tea the bearer cleared the table and removed the cloth, revealing a polished teak surface with a brass plate bearing the bold inscription:

FRANCIS THEOBALD le GRANGE
1872 –
Served India with love and pride

'Is this table a retirement gift?' asked Charles, impressed.
'Yes . . . You could say that.'
'Why wasn't the date of your retirement filled in?'
'It will be done shortly.'
Charles and I exchanged surreptitious glances as we realized we were looking at the old man's coffin.

Chapter IV

Alarums and Excursions

he honking of migrating geese was a magical sound because it heralded the advent of cooler weather. After months of being confined by torrential rain and oppressive heat, people made the most of the cooler months from mid-October and toured the countryside. The Tour was one of the great institutions of the Raj for it helped to bridge the gap between divergent cultures. In almost every occupation, the annual tour was an essential duty; it was the opportunity for a district officer to attend to a multitude of needs and problems, and put a finger on the pulse of the district. He often travelled for weeks at a stretch, for hundreds of miles in isolated areas. He usually toured on horseback and his retinue travelled by a variety of methods depending on the district and the terrain. Inevitably it was a leisurely time, at the pace of the bullock or elephant. Few outlying areas could be reached by car; roads, if any, were hazardous and gouged out by the steel-rimmed wheels of bullock-carts.

Within weeks of our arrival in Rampur, we started preparing for a six-week tour of the district. An official tour with a retinue of orderlies, clerks and assistants, a *dak-wallah*[1] a *syce*,[2] and numerous porters is no small undertaking; but with a family of five, household staff and pets tagged on, it grows to prodigious proportions. The excitement of the preparations infected the household like a fever.

1   *dak-wallah*: messenger; mail bearer.
2   *syce*: groom.

Assisting the tonga.

Everyone was involved in checking the camping equipment and packing. Lamps were trimmed, provisions collected, clothes and linen sorted out. Each day more trunks, boxes and bundles were piled up in readiness. Ruthlessly I hauled out non-essentials, for Charles had emphasized the need to keep the load down.

I had given Ayah a limited list of the children's requirements but their heavy bulging suitcases evoked suspicion. My probing revealed all sorts of junk packed among their clothes, particularly in Michael's case. There was a selection of crude materials – scrap metal, string, cotton reels and suchlike – with which he presumably intended to make models or toys for he was an inventive child. In addition, he had carefully packed his prize collection of stones and a catapult made by one of the servants.

'*Arébaprébap* Memsahib! The *butchas* are very naughty. Three times have I checked the cases and removed such things.' I wondered uncomfortably whether my children's unsophisticated treasures were a reflection of their deprivation as they had very few toys or personal possessions. But I consoled myself that the benefits gained from their experiences outweighed the disadvantages of living in outlying districts.

The camping paraphernalia, luggage for the multitude and numerous containers of provisions were loaded on to the bullock-carts. With noisy exhortations and much whip-cracking, toe-prodding and tail-twisting, the clumsy beasts were spurred into action and the carts moved off slowly with axles groaning. The accompanying procession walked or cycled alongside. Nestles, our little *deshi*[1] cow, on whom we depended for milk during the tour, remained close to her calf who rode in state like a golden idol on one of the carts. It was a cavalcade worthy of the spacious days of The Great Moguls.[2]

The family party followed the next day in a tonga. Drawn by a pair of large humped racing-bullocks, it could move at the relatively cracking pace of eight miles an hour. Ayah and the girls sat in comparative comfort at the back with Powder, the cat, in her travelling basket at their feet. The dogs, Kim and Tess, yapping with excitement, took up vantage points at the sides. Michael, who was a seasoned traveller, sat beside Hira Lal on the raised box-seat, alert and ready to assist the *tonga-wallah*. With a jingle of harness-bells and a chorus of raucous curses ably led by Michael, the tonga moved off briskly, lanterns swaying precariously underneath.

Charles and I led the way on horseback. My mount, Rangar, a gentle bay with a sensitive mouth, had been an excellent polo pony in his day. Charles' Kathiawar pony, Nilgai, was a large mettlesome animal that had been used for pig-sticking and only the best of riders

---

1 *deshi*: country; hybrid.
2 The Great Moguls: the emperors of Delhi in the sixteenth to nineteenth
   centuries.

Bullock-cart struggling through a dry river bed.

Tonga crossing a river.

could manage her. The tonga rattled and bumped, churning up choking dust and coating everything in fine red powder. The road soon narrowed to a rough track through eroded scrub with an occasional cultivated patch of cotton or *jawar*, the staple food of the area. Scrawny cattle sought the meagre pasture and enterprising goats reached up on hind legs for leaves of stunted thorn trees. Graceless vultures feeding on a rotting carcass rose ponderously at our approach and settled on branches, waiting to resume their meal.

Barely five miles on, a lone cyclist, pedalling hard, caught up with us. He was wearing the familiar blue serge uniform of the Police. I looked at Charles in dismay. It must be an urgent message, perhaps a war emergency or a Hindu-Muslim riot. I imagined being recalled with all haste to Headquarters, the whole expedition cancelled. The messenger leapt off his bicycle and saluted smartly. From the large official sack he gravely produced two parcels: a bundle of clean clothes delivered by the *dhobi*[1] to the office after our departure, and a large packet addressed to me in Jane Carstairs' untidy writing. Inside were the voluminous *Gone with the Wind*, a few copies of *Blackwoods*, my favourite magazine, and an Army and Navy Stores' catalogue, that somewhat fanciful and tenuous connection with the outer world. 'You've probably read the book, but you may like to read it again,' Jane had scrawled hastily. 'The magazines have just arrived and I thought you may like to browse through the new Christmas catalogue.'

'How kind and thoughtful of Jane!' I exclaimed, delighted to have something to occupy my leisure hours, but Charles was not amused.

'No reply!' he informed the constable curtly. With another smart salute, the messenger mounted his iron steed and retraced his dusty tracks.

T̲he radio, which was an essential link with civilization during these remote tours, was singled out for special treatment as it

---

1 *dhobi*: washerman; laundry servant.

The Police-Sahib welcomed by the village band and garlanded.

would not have survived the rough journey on the bullock-carts. The large cumbersome unit was slung on a pole and carried by two coolies[1] with all the deference shown to a Maharajah in a litter. The heavy battery was given a special place on the tonga for its energy had to be carefully preserved. Normally charged by the car or the police bus, the battery became progressively more feeble as the tour proceeded.

Hira Lal took a proprietary interest in the radio and tolerated with a superior smile the villagers who crowded round to listen in awe to the incomprehensible sounds from the miraculous equipment. 'They are *jungli admi*[2] and do not know any better. What can one expect of such fools?' he said scornfully. In fact, Charles and I were almost as delighted as the *jungli admi* when the radio produced any sound at all after its ordeals. Snatches of music or a few cheerful words between atmospherics were thrilling, though fragments of news could be misleading and caused much speculation.

Villagers usually got wind of our approach well in advance and a welcoming party would meet us on the road. We were sometimes heralded by pipes and drums or garlanded with marigolds. Water would be offered from brass *lotas* which the women balanced adroitly on their heads, but parched though we were, we dared not drink water that was likely to be contaminated and merely made a polite pretence at it. Government officers were forbidden to accept gifts other than fruit and flowers. This was known as the *phal-phul*[3] rule and it was a protection against bribery which was common practice among petitioners. But it was conventional for an Indian to present a *nazar* to an officer as a token of respect and goodwill. Usually, he would offer a rupee on his open palm; the officer would touch it and immediately remit it.

On arrival at a village, the police orderlies conferred with the headmen to arrange an official meeting. The reception was normally

---

1   coolie: unskilled labourer; porter.
2   *jungli admi*: wild or uncivilized men.
3   *phal-phul*: lit. fruit and flowers.

held under the great village tree, usually a holy peepul or a banyan, whose huge umbrellas afforded widespread shade. The visiting party sat with the headman and *zemindars*[1] at a crude table while all the villagers squatted at a polite distance. Invariably we met with the warmest hospitality and the utmost deference, for the infrequent visits of the Police-Sahib were opportunities to air grievances, resolve disputes and request favours. Refreshments were usually offered, sometimes a modest mug of tea, sometimes a lavish feast of goat slaughtered for the occasion. The leisurely discourse in Marathi[2] followed an unchanging pattern: first an enquiry about health, then a discussion of the weather and the crops followed by an exchange of news. Finally, there was a polite and dignified relay of complaints and requests.

While touring his district an officer made himself accessible to the humblest petitioner and was never off duty. From early morning queues waited patiently at the camp, and Charles spent a large part of his time in tedious and often fruitless discussions about frivolous or false complaints. Disputes were usually over women, property, cattle-thieving or damage to crops. Such infringements often provoked excessive reactions and criminal assaults; it was not uncommon for a man to kill another for stealing his buffalo.

At a remote village we were met by a group of women dressed like *banjaras*[3] with exposed midriffs and gaudy voluminous skirts. The Sub-Inspector established that they were not the bold thieving gypsies who were universally disliked and feared. Chattering and laughing, they crowded round our tonga like a flock of gaily-plumaged birds. They had rarely seen white women and gasped in admiration at Susan's ash-blonde hair, the bolder ones stroking it tentatively as if to ascertain that it was real. At a word from their menfolk they retreated submissively, but from time to time they

---

1 *zemindar*: landowner, usually wealthy with influence in his community.
2 Marathi: it was compulsory for members of the ICS and Indian Police to learn a classical language such as Hindi or Urdu, as well as the local dialect, in this case Marathi.
3 *banjaras*: gypsies.

Villagers garland the Police-Memsahib

appeared at the fringes of the camp, with saris pulled over their faces, to steal another look.

On one occasion a reception was given for us by a wealthy *zemindar*. We were ceremoniously garlanded with freshly-picked marigolds, those colourful, if unfragrant, blooms always used for such occasions. As we took our places at the table spread with appetizing dishes, the rank odour of the flowers almost overpowered the aromatic spices.

'Do you think we could take the garlands off while we eat?' I whispered to Charles.

'No! That would offend our host. We'll get rid of them as soon as possible.'

Our sufferance brought reward. The *zemindar*, in appreciation of our company and interest in his concerns, offered the use of elephants to help with transport. The bullock-carts had become bogged down by recent heavy rain and the terrain was hazardous for the horses. However, elephants could plough through the mud, their massive feet sinking deep and emerging with loud squelches. I sat with Ayah and the children on a mattress atop Ganesh Bahadu,[1] enjoying the leisurely swaying motion and the splendid views from twelve feet up. '*Chelo! Chelo!*'[2] urged the mahout,[3] but the gentle giant would not be hurried except when goaded by the dogs or horses.

There is nothing quite like the satisfaction of journey's end in camp. When one arrives hot, exhausted and caked in dust, a bath, even in a small tin tub smelling of woodsmoke, is sheer luxury. Far from the amenities of civilization, what greater indulgence could there be on such an evening than a long, cold drink? Hira Lal always managed to provide drinks chilled in an earthenware *gharah* while we

---

1 Ganesh: Hindu God of Protection, an elephant-headed deity;
Bahadu: honorary address.
2 *Chelo!*: Move! Hurry up!
3 mahout: elephant keeper/rider.

waited for our meal. The aroma of meat cooking over red-hot coals stimulated soaring appetites and nothing, it seemed, could taste better than venison, wild duck or partridge shot *en route*, or fresh murrel caught in a nearby stream. These simple sensuous pleasures promoted feelings of deep contentment and well-being, which we rarely found anywhere else. This was the India which we loved: unsophisticated, unspoiled and completely at one with nature.

Our first campsite was in a shady grove of banyan trees near a stream. The dense jungle, teeming with wild life, pressed closely so we were careful to be in camp well before dusk. Pug marks along the banks showed evidence of tigers, panthers, bears and many other animals which drank at dawn and dusk. Among the most threatening predators were wild dogs which killed indiscriminately and devoured voraciously every morsel, as indicated by the fur and claws in their droppings. Stealthy scavenging jackals, which usually hunted in packs for small prey, were relatively harmless but their blood-curdling yells and plaintive baying could be heard throughout the night. The weird repetitive cry of a lone jackal or *phiaou* was ominous because it warned of a tiger or panther on the kill, but the most disturbing sounds were the demonic falsetto shrieks and giggles of hyenas.

Our dogs, who would have been easy victims, were secured to the poles inside the tent at night. Sometimes we woke up to find them straining at their leashes, hackles raised in terror, as they followed the stealthy movements of a panther or hyena on the other side of the canvas. Powder crouched unconcernedly beside me, secure in the knowledge that she could scale a pole or tree if need arose. Unlike most cats, she accepted the frequent change of domicile with equanimity, establishing a happy hunting-ground wherever she went.

Our spacious tent was like a big top, divided into a large living-room, two bedrooms and another compartment which Charles used as his office. *Dhurries* were spread on the ground over a covering of straw and gave a homely and comfortable feeling. The strong canvas, about twenty feet high, and the stout guy ropes were ideal for acrobatics. The children became adept performers emulating the

Hindu villager and Ayah with missy-baba

primates in the surrounding trees, undeterred by occasional mishaps. The monkeys were usually unconcerned by these human invasions; indeed, they enjoyed teasing and abusing us, chattering noisily and bombarding us with fruit. Brazen members of the troop would creep under the awnings and stealthily open bins and packages to steal provisions.

One afternoon, alerted by angry shouting, I rushed out of the tent to see the servants racing in a body towards the jungle, shouting and brandishing sticks, presumably chasing marauders. The children, who had been playing in the open grassland nearby, were nowhere to be seen and I wondered whether they had been swept along with the excited pursuers. They were usually in the forefront of any action.

'Where are the babas?' I called anxiously.

'*Bandar-log!*'[1] gasped Hira Lal over his shoulder.

'Never mind the *bandar-log!* Where are the babas?' But my question was unheard for Hira Lal, normally so deferential, had obviously been incited to action by the thieves. Feeling uneasy in case the children had been caught up in the fray, I hastened after the assailants. When

---

1   *bandar-log*: monkeys.

I arrived at the noisy confrontation, the servants were lashing out at a large troop of enraged and aggressive macaques.

'Leave them alone! They're dangerous!' I shouted, but the servants were bent on destruction in most uncharacteristic fashion. The red-faced macaques, which are known to be bad-tempered and vicious, stood their ground, grimacing and barking menacingly. The large fearless males, goaded into retaliation, were ready to attack.

'Leave them!' I yelled again, amazed and annoyed by the servants' persistence. Suddenly, I caught sight of the three children in the background, almost encircled by the beasts. Susan and Judy were clinging to each other and sobbing in terror while Michael was pelting the monkeys with stones to ward them off. Numb with fear and anxiety, I watched helplessly while the servants continued the onslaught. Eventually, the animals retreated and the children were snatched to safety.

The walls of the small, roofless bathing tent were just high enough to shield the vulnerable occupant from curious eyes, though one was not entirely safe from unwanted guests. Snakes and scorpions, attracted by the warm, humid atmosphere, crawled under the sides and distorted shadows of animals danced on the canvas in the flickering lamplight. Nevertheless, the woodsmoke-scented water was relaxing even when sitting with knees up to one's chin in the small tin tub.

When my sister, Barbara, had been with us on a previous tour, I cautioned her. 'Take a bright lamp with you and watch where you tread. The creepie-crawlies come out in the evening when it's cool. And stand on the wooden board when you get out of the bath.'

Barbara shuddered. 'I think I'll take two lamps if you can spare them. Would you mind staying within earshot? I'll be as quick as possible.' Within a surprisingly short time she was back, wrapped in a bath towel.

'Did you enjoy your bath? You needn't have rushed. No scorpions, I hope?'

'No . . . but there were some animals outside,' she said, agitated. 'Their shadows were bobbing up and down but I couldn't work out what they were.'

Charles looked up from his papers. 'Don't worry. They wouldn't hurt you. They're just fascinated by your shadow.'

'But what animals . . . ?'

'Villagers,' he said succinctly. 'You know how curious they are!'

After their morning lessons the children were playing 'Man-eaters', their favourite game. As usual, Michael was the tiger prowling around the tent and the girls were the victims cowering within. I listened to the growls and squeals as I reclined under the shady awning, browsing through the Christmas catalogue which Jane had sent me. I indulged in thoughts of a traditional English Christmas and the sophisticated toys and games which might have a civilizing effect on the children.

It had become quiet inside the tent so I assumed that the man-eater had finished harrying his victims and had gone in search of further adventure. Suddenly, a breathless Michael appeared from the direction of the servants' camp.

'Mum, Cook was nearly killed by a tiger last night!'

'Who? Mohammed Ali? Is he all right?' I imagined him writhing in pain with his leg bitten off. 'What happened?' I asked anxiously.

'It was a man-eater.'

'Oh, Lord! Where is he now?' As I spoke, I saw a procession approaching, and to my great relief it was led by the cook himself with all limbs intact. The hero described in a tremulous voice the ordeal which he had suffered, his sympathetic supporters interjecting colourful details so that the story grew in the telling. While travelling on the bullock-cart through the jungle, they had been followed by a tiger whose eyes, as big as moons, had been focused on Mohammed Ali. Throughout the night he had kept watch while his companions slept, for it was clear that he had been singled out as the next victim.

'If it is the will of Allah that I am eaten by a tiger, so be it!' he concluded dramatically.

'Are you sure it was a tiger?' I questioned, for it seemed that any self-respecting tiger would prefer a plump and more easily procurable bullock to the skinny cook.

'Perhaps it was a hyena,' volunteered the humble *masalchee*.

Mohammed Ali rounded on his assistant with scorn. 'Did you not see the stripes? Or hear the growls?'

'Perhaps I was asleep, *Khansama-ji*,'[1] he answered meekly. 'It is as you say.'

'I kept watch last night so you would be safe,' Mohammed Ali reminded him sharply.

Michael had followed the conversation with interest. 'I've got a good idea. Let's catch the tiger by making a trap with Mohammed Ali. Of course, we'll rescue him before the tiger gets him,' he added quickly.

The assembled company laughed heartily but Mohammed Ali was offended. 'Who will cook your food if I am killed, Michael-baba?'

'Michael! Apologize immediately!' I reprimanded, suppressing a smile. I assured Mohammed Ali that the Sahib would investigate the matter and take action to ensure their safety.

After a few days we moved on to the next village about ten miles away where we had arranged to stay in a dak-bungalow. We were met by agitated villagers who had been terrorized for some time by a tiger. The animal had snatched several goats and had recently killed a woman drawing water from the river. It was assumed that the Police-Sahib, protector and defender of the poor, would rid them of the menace.

A rude *machan*[2] was constructed in the fork of a large leafy mango tree along the path to the river where the tiger's spoor had been seen.

---

1 *Khansama-ji*: respectful address.
2 *machan*: shooting platform.

A young goat was tethered beneath the tree to raise the alarm and the track was swept with fresh branches to mask human odours. Charles and the headman took up their positions on the *machan* in the late afternoon before nocturnal animals emerged.

The dak-bungalow overlooked the nullah along which animals were likely to migrate towards the water. Michael, disappointed that he was not allowed on the *machan*, had his pellet-gun at the ready to protect his mother and sisters. We watched through the dusty windows, listening for a shot. In the gathering dusk the thirsty inhabitants of the jungle, hunters and hunted in uneasy truce, made their way in sedate procession towards the river: timid deer nervously sniffing the air, a clutch of noisy peafowl, a herd of wild pig, a shambling bear, stealthy jackals, all with the same purpose.

A waxing moon inched across the horizon, silvering the tops of trees and casting shadows which shifted like wary animals. The charged atmosphere was intoxicating to fertile imaginations. The children could see animals of every kind in place of boulders and shrubs . . .

Suddenly, a large form emerged from a thicket and moved unhurriedly along the track towards the *machan*. It ignored the terror-stricken goat which strained and bleated piteously, and proceeded down the nullah towards the village. There was no doubting its intention. The single shot from Charles' powerful .375 Mannlicher found its mark and the beast collapsed soundlessly.

Summoned by blasts on the whistle, the villagers thronged out exultantly. The dreaded killer, a toothless old female driven to seeking easy prey as is often the case with man-eaters, was slung between poles and borne away in triumph. Sounds of revelry could be heard late into the night for not only had the village been delivered from danger, but there was bounty to be shared. Charles was proclaimed a hero and was later awarded the mangy skin.

It was common practice to sell young animals to soft-hearted memsahibs, who were known to give generous sums to save the orphans. A villager hoping to make a few rupees in this way was severely mauled by an enraged tigress while attempting to steal her apparently unguarded cubs. He almost died from loss of blood, and the gaping wound in his buttock was dangerously open to infection. However, he made a miraculous recovery and was well enough to walk just a few weeks later.

Charles sent for the man, who limped into his office. Lowering his *dhoti*,[1] he revealed a huge, raw wound. However it was clean and obviously healing well.

Charles was aghast. 'Was this man taken to the dispensary for treatment?' he asked the Sub-Inspector.

'No, Sahib. He himself attended to the wound.'

'But there is great risk of tetanus and other infections.'

'There is no more danger, Sahib.'

'But has he had *any* medical help?' Charles persisted.

'He himself was knowing what to do, Sahib. As you will observe, the wound is almost healed.'

Charles was incredulous. 'What did he treat the wound with?'

'With cow dung alone, Sahib. It is the best remedy.'

Fires had been breaking out unaccountably in the district of Bijapur. Huts and haystacks suddenly ignited, usually at dusk, causing panic and suffering. Fires were usually caused by unguarded lamps in huts or by spontaneous combustion resulting from great heat generated within a haystack, but the superstitious folk believed that a *bhoot*[2] was to blame.

Our arrival was greeted with great joy for the villagers believed that the Police-Sahib would solve the mystery. The strange phenomenon was discussed throughout the camp, and as dusk approached we waited for the alert. As soon as alarmed shouts of 'Fire!' were heard, the servants, orderlies and children grabbed all available lanterns and

---

1   *dhoti*: loin-cloth worn by Hindus.
2   *bhoot*: ghost.

torches and raced in a body to the village. Only Charles was left in darkness, in the bath. Hearing the noise and confusion, he groped for his shorts and boots which were fortunately close at hand, and set out in pursuit. A red glow lit up the sky and he struck a direct line towards it, but the night was dark and the ground was rough. A shallow disused well, partially filled with rubble, lay in his path and into this he fell with a resounding thump. When he arrived at the village, bruised and dishevelled, it was rumoured that the brave Sahib had had a tussle with the *bhoot* who was clearly a powerful opponent.

By fortunate coincidence the fires ceased thereafter. The villagers were greatly impressed by Charles' supernatural powers, while Charles reckoned that his broken ribs were a small price to have paid to evict the fictitious *bhoot*.

When the usual diet of goat or chicken palled, we would go in search of something else for the pot: duck, peafowl, guinea fowl or *jungli moorgi*, a gaily-plumaged wildfowl so much more tasty than its domesticated cousin. The Sub-Inspector informed us that there was an abundance of fowl at the nearby *jheel*.[1] Two villagers guided us for several miles along twisting paths through featureless scrub and fields of cotton.

'Is it much further?' I enquired after I had stubbed my toe. I was concerned that my limping would slow down the others.

'Just a short way, Memsahib.'

Distances are gauged by the briskness of pace and the hazards along the route, and I realized that the *jheel* could still be a considerable distance away. 'You go on,' I called to the others. 'I'll rest for a bit.'

'All right. Be back in half an hour or so, I expect,' Charles answered, quickening his pace. The sun was low in the sky and they would have to hurry.

The Sub-Inspector instructed one of the guides to remain with me, explaining that the Memsahib needed to rest. Thankfully I settled

---

1 *jheel*: small lake or pond.

down on a rotten log, the only available seat in the barren scrub. The guide squatted on his haunches at a respectful distance in the typical posture of repose, preparing to wait with timeless patience. He watched me curiously as though I were performing an extraordinary act, and indeed he was well rewarded for I soon leapt up with a startled cry to escape an army of scorpions with stinging tails poised.

As I hobbled towards a tree, I interpreted my guardian's agitation as an expression of sympathy and responded with gratitude. Then, leaning against the trunk to take the weight off my painful foot, I noticed a host of vicious red ants, nippers bared, ascending the trunk. Without dignity, I sank on to a tussock of grass, conceding that the wisdom of the unsophisticated yokel far surpassed my own in matters of rural lore. He gave a broad approving grin like an indulgent teacher whose slow-witted pupil has eventually grasped an obvious principle. By that time he was calm and rested, and rose to scan the horizon for the returning party.

Suddenly he pointed with his *lathi*[1] towards a patch of stunted cotton bushes and exclaimed loudly, '*Rooyee! Rooyee!*' He spat at a beetle a few yards away as if to emphasize his point. I realized he was showing me his own cotton crop where the bolls were on the point of bursting. At least I knew that *rooyee* was the word for cotton.

'So it is,' I agreed amicably. There seemed to be a new understanding between us and I appreciated his attempt to make conversation.

'*Rooyee! Rooyee!*' he cried again, more emphatically.

'Yes, I see,' I answered in Hindi. 'You have a good harvest.' The pain in my toe had eased off and I felt more relaxed.

Suddenly, from beyond the cotton field, a couple of large brown bears shambled towards us. At the same moment Charles and the others appeared at a run from another direction.

'For goodness' sake, run! They're trying to cut us off,' gasped Charles. The bears were advancing slowly in a cunning manoeuvre

---

1 *lathi*: stick or club.

The police bus in difficulty.

to get between us and the rest of the party. He fired a warning shot. The bears, dangerously close, dropped to all fours and shuffled off.

'Even I could hear that man warning you!' Charles expostulated. 'Don't you know that *rooyee* means "bear"?'[1]

---

1   *rooyee*: cotton (Hindi), similar in sound to *reech*, 'a bear' in Marathi, the local dialect.

After several weeks on tour, the arrival of a *dak-wallah* bringing mail, news and supplies was greeted with eagerness. The brief contact with home and the outside world was exciting and we were hungry for news, no matter how trivial. However, after two days of travelling in the heat on dusty roads by bicycle and bus – with the bicycle on the roof – the supplies looked inedible and the clean laundry needed rewashing.

In our absence, Charles' *munshi*[1] attended to routine business but could not make decisions about domestic matters and referred these to us. A chronicle of disasters was related. The *mali* informed us that our vegetables had been trampled by a *badmash's* cows and requested more seeds as though they were easily procurable. The *dhobi* reported that our well-worn sheets had finally disintegrated. The *masalchee's* wife complained she had no food and had had to sell her silver bracelets. Blankets had been stolen from Mohammed Ali's quarters. There was no good news.

We relayed instructions to avert the crises – wage advances, replacements and consolatory messages. After the *dak-wallah's* departure, we were glad to return to domestic oblivion.

Towards the end of our tour we received a police message informing us of the tragic death of Hira Lal's eldest child. Ten-year-old Budhoo had cut her palm with a rusty knife and had developed tetanus. Charles cancelled the rest of the tour and we made plans for our immediate return. It was arranged that Kisnia and Hira Lal, who was deeply shocked, would go ahead as quickly as possible. Then Kisnia would return with the car to meet the family at a dak-bungalow.

All dak-bungalows are alike, having been built from a master plan devised in the last century. In the front garden of this one, the large stone wheel that had been used to grind the mortar for the building was preserved like an historic monument, and the circular track of

---

1 *munshi*: secretary/clerk.

Dak-bungalow

the bullocks as they dragged the heavy wheel had been permanently scored into the ground. The rest-house seemed palatial after our many weeks under canvas. It was equipped with all the essential amenities in varying states of repair. Beds with lumpy coir mattresses and mosquito nets with large holes offering easy access to flying insects, were not conducive to a good night's rest. Coarse, chipped crockery, like battle-scarred veterans, dutifully persisted in service safeguarded by a threatening list of fines for breakages. In contrast, the bathroom china was refined and elegant with matching basin, jug and soap-dish. The chamber-pot, decorated with love-knots, roses and forget-me-nots, was like a graceful Grecian urn. Indeed, its intended purpose seemed profane.

As Charles relaxed on the verandah in a long-sleever,[1] a visitor was announced.

1 long-sleever: reclining cane chair with long arms.

'Khan Sahib is highly respected citizen of Jamargh,' explained the Sub-Inspector. 'He is aiding and abetting the police in every particular!'

Mustapa Khan was a tall distinguished man with piercing eyes under beetling brows and had the red-dyed beard of a *hadji*.[1] He and Charles were soon locked in animated conversation for he was certainly not the run-of-the-mill *malguzar*[2] wielding a grievance, but a cultured lawyer with a keen sense of humour and a shrewd grasp of world affairs. A man of influence in the village, he had come to *salaam-wasti*[3] and to acquaint Charles with local affairs.

Before leaving, he turned to me with a courtly bow. 'My wife will be honoured if Memsahib visits her. It will be a very great pleasure to welcome you to our humble house.'

'He has four official wives as befits all Mohammedans of rank,' Charles told me later. 'But you'll probably meet only the senior one.'

The following day I went by tonga to the house on the outskirts of the village. The garish yellow double-storey was surrounded by a high brick wall of the same colour. The strictly purdah[4] household was cloistered and silent. I felt uneasy as I was led by an elderly male retainer across the empty courtyard. After passing through a series of gloomy, shuttered rooms to an inner courtyard, I was handed over like a chattel to an unsmiling maidservant. In a moment of panic, I wondered whether I was about to become the next wife of the Khan Sahib, confined for ever in this uncanny house. Where were all his children? I knew that Mustapa Khan had eighteen legitimate ones and many others besides. I thought of the noise and confusion made by my three children and felt sneaking admiration for a family of dozens who could live in such peace and quiet.

The senior wife, Begum Khan,[5] was awaiting my arrival in the curtained *zenana*[6] chamber. We greeted each other by a mere touching

---

1   *hadji*: a Muslim who had made the pilgrimage to Mecca.
2   *malguzar*: headman; tax-collector.
3   *salaam-wasti*: pay respects.
4   purdah: seclusion of Indian women from public view; veil or curtain.
5   Begum: courtesy title for lady of high rank; princess.
6   *zenana*: secluded place for women only.

of the palms, a concession to Western custom. Her attendants and children crouched on the cushioned floor, transfixed and expressionless. Welcome or not, it was impossible to tell, but clearly I was an object of curiosity. One by one, the older children were pushed into the arena to meet me but they stood with hanging heads, overawed and unable to respond to my greetings. I wondered where the other wives and children were confined but was not long left in doubt. As I looked around I was met by unblinking stares from numerous slits in the surrounding purdahs. Heavy breathing from my large audience created an atmosphere of theatrical tension as my hostess and I struggled for words. Obviously it was up to me to keep the conversational ball rolling. Recalling the advice I had been given to cope with such a social crisis – enquire about health, childbirth, children and food, in that order – I solicitously asked Begum Khan about her health. It was like pressing a switch. The current immediately began to flow and all I had to do was sit back and listen to an animated and graphic account of her afflictions. She appeared to suffer from ailments of every kind – muscular pains, digestive complaints, breathing disorders, child-bearing difficulties – but she bore her adversities stoically for it was the will of Allah that she should suffer. Nor had her children been spared as each of them had dreadful problems to contend with. Obviously their glowing complexions and bright eyes belied their poor health. She described each child's maladies at length and I felt relieved that the other wives and their many offspring were not present, at least not officially, so that I was spared the painful details of their ailments.

The arrival of refreshments was such a welcome diversion that I tucked into the rich sweetmeats with uncharacteristic eagerness, much to the delight of my hostess who pressed more and more upon me. Reverting to the obsessive subject of health, she enquired politely after mine just as the first pangs of indigestion were striking.

'Well, my stomach hurts at present,' I answered truthfully.

'Yes, after the birth of three children, Memsahib must surely be suffering. Alas! That is the lot of us poor women. It is the will of Allah!'

The women clucked and sighed in sympathy, the breathing all around grew heavier and the purdahs bulged with the weight of bodies as my spectators moved in to hear the interesting disclosures I was about to make. Many had more or less emerged from their screens, curiosity having overcome discretion, and I was the centre of a rapt audience. I certainly could not disappoint them now.

'My legs ache sometimes,' I continued, remembering the stiffness caused by riding after long absences. I was beginning to enjoy the attention and sympathy which I did not usually receive from my family. I considered describing the unpleasant symptoms I had suffered from typhoid and malaria but decided that the tension would become unbearable. Instead, I commiserated about the vagaries of Allah, and when it was time to leave we exchanged heartfelt wishes for improved health all round. The Khan Sahib, she told me, was very well; in fact, he was the only healthy member of his large family. Anyway, I reflected, there was certainly no doubt about his virility.

We spent several days at the dak-bungalow while Charles completed his business. It was an uninteresting place with little to amuse the children and it therefore provided a good opportunity for lessons. The first morning they were up early and disappeared to explore the area. With Kisnia's help, I eventually found Susan and Judy absorbed in making mud pies by a stream, with Ayah in attendance. The *khansama's* wife was washing clothes in a rock pool nearby, scrubbing and thumping them mercilessly on a rock as she shrilly recounted local gossip. On the opposite bank a group of young boys, strangely quiet and well-behaved, was gathered around Michael who was distinguishable by his topee.

Kisnia assessed the scene and grinned broadly. '*Chota Kaptaan Sahib* is training new recruits,' he explained. Michael marshalled the boys into lines and proceeded to drill them with loud clear commands in the manner of an experienced sergeant major.

'Where do these boys come from?' I asked in amazement.

'The *chokras* are from the police lines, Memsahib. Michael-baba is telling the Head Constable's son that if they are wishing to become policemen, they must first take training with him.'

'But surely they don't believe that!'

Kisnia shrugged. 'There is no harm and much good in what Michael-baba does.'

They won't stand it for long, I thought. But each day after breakfast Michael, neatly dressed in khaki shorts and shirt, went to meet his squad who were lined up eagerly awaiting his orders.

On the day of our departure we packed into our little car for the last lap of the journey back to Headquarters. Michael's recruits were nowhere to be seen and he was obviously disappointed. However, as we drove off we saw them standing to attention in two lines on either side of the road, their stick-rifles at the slope, saluting their young commander. On the front seat beside me, his little face set and inscrutable, Michael acknowledged their salute with a touch of his topee.

Police Orderly Kisnia in the back seat murmured approvingly, '*Shabash!*¹ *Chota Kaptaan Sahib, salaam!*'

---

1 '*Shabash!*': 'Well done!'.

Chapter V

Forces at Work and Rest

 Muslim wandering in the vicinity of the temple had been molested and injured by a group of Hindus, and the case was about to come to Court. Shankar Dhagat, a learned and respected lawyer, came to the bungalow to discuss the matter with Charles.

'Of course, I am impartial,' the lawyer said solemnly, 'It is clear the Mussulman[1] was provoking trouble but we Hindus try to be tolerant.'

Suddenly Shankar Dhagat noticed a clay figurine on the shelf. 'Sahib, is that not a figure of our Mahatma?'[2] he asked incredulously, a sharp edge to his voice.

Charles studied the small ornament which he had hardly noticed before. Bought from an itinerant vendor, it was an innocuous little model of a typical villager in a *dhoti* with a load of faggots on his head. The semi-naked figure was indeed reminiscent of Gandhi. Charles sensed the lawyer's disapproval for what appeared to be an irreverent disrespect for the Mahatma, for the figurine was finely veiled in dust and vying for space on the cluttered shelf.

'The Mahatma should have due attention and respect unless you wish evil to befall him!' Shankar Dhagat said boldly.

Charles concealed his irritation with an effort and assured the lawyer that he harboured no ill will against Gandhi. 'Anyway, that isn't a model of the Mahatma. I've never heard of him carrying wood on his head. Have you?'

---

1 Mussulman: derogatory term for a Muslim.
2 Mahatma: a person regarded with reverence, in this case Gandhi.

'No menial task is below our Mahatma, Sahib.'

'Well, spinning certainly—' muttered Charles.

'That is so, Sahib. Our Mahatma is humble and worthy of respect.' Shankar Dhagat was unconvinced by Charles' explanation and was clearly disturbed. The purpose of his visit forgotten, he rose to take his leave and Charles hastened him on his way.

'I don't hold out much hope for the poor Muslim in this court case,' said Charles later. 'As for Gandhi, we'd better lock him up in a cupboard so he can't cause any more trouble!'

During a visit to a remote encampment of the Pioneer Corps we were invited to dine at the officers' mess.

'I apologize for the uninteresting meal,' said the Commanding Officer, Major Dickson. 'It's the usual stew made from imported tinned foods. We eat this sort of thing almost every day.'

'Please don't apologize,' I said with feeling. 'It's a real treat for us.'

'Really?'

'Oh, yes. We very seldom see tinned food. We have to make do with tough old chicken and whatever vegetables we can grow. Or goat as a treat. Even rice is hard to get. Sometimes we buy tins of corned beef or spam which have been thrown from the troop trains and picked up by beggars.'

'Well, fancy that! I suppose we're really quite well off.'

The tasty stew of spam and vegetables was followed by tinned fruit and rounded off with Kraft cheese.

'*Kraft cheese!*' Charles tucked in heartily for this was a favourite which he had not seen for years.

We thanked our hosts profusely for the delicious meal. 'You're very welcome,' said the Major. 'It's a pleasure to see people enjoying the food. We have more supplies than we need so you're doing us a favour.'

An outdoor cinema show followed the meal. Dark threatening clouds did not deter the men who were used to being outside in all weathers. They equipped us with mackintoshes, gumboots and umbrellas which gave us a sense of involvement in the underwater adventure on the screen. Soon the film was barely visible through the watery pall while the soundtrack could not compete with the drumming rain and monsoon toads. Our protective garments were inadequate defence and we became soaked and chilly.

As we ploughed through the slippery morass to the dak-bungalow, nursing colds, we consoled ourselves that the benefits gained from the occasion far outweighed our temporary indisposition. Heaped in the back of the car were large supplies of spam and corned beef, tinned fruit, strawberry jam, chocolate and Kraft cheese.

A small army camp had been established at Arna, a remote spot where Chindits[1] were training in rough jungle conditions for operations against the Japanese in Burma and Assam. Arna lay in Charles' district, near the dak-bungalow where we were spending the night. When we called in to check that all was well, we were warmly welcomed by the Colonel and invited to dine the following day.

As we approached I took quick stock of the surroundings. The children would undoubtedly rush off to explore and I felt concerned when I saw the deep river gorge and the dark foreboding jungle, which were the training grounds for the soldiers. But there was scarcely time to caution the children, for as we drew to a halt the car doors were opened by our eager hosts and the children and dogs tumbled out unceremoniously.

'Quite safe here,' we were assured as the children raced off in a body with the intrepid Michael in the lead, deaf to our warnings.

'But, it may rain—' I knew that the innocent stream at the bottom of the gorge could become a raging torrent within minutes if there were a downpour.

'Don't worry. After all, we've been here for months and we're still alive. We can watch the kids from up here.'

---

1 Chindits: members of the Allied forces behind the Japanese lines in Burma (1943–5).

The Colonel led us to one of the neatly thatched bashas[1] perched near the edge of the gorge. From the verandah there was a commanding view of the stream a hundred feet below.

'How long would it take you to get to the bottom?' I asked anxiously, visualizing the girls being swept away by the current.

'Just thirty seconds!' responded a tough sergeant with a grin.

I felt slightly mollified. 'What about the jungle? It must be full of dangers.' The dense jungle surrounded the camp like a monster about to engulf its prey. Brilliant blooms of the paras tree, the flame-of-the-forest, protruded like scarlet tongues from the darkness.

'There certainly are a few unexpected hazards in there.'

'What if the children—?'

'Don't worry! That young man of yours seems to know what he's doing. They'll have a marvellous time.'

The men regaled us with tales of their narrow escapes during their treacherous exercises. The most experienced Chindit clearly needed all his strength and expertise to battle against the surging river, to defend himself against a cobra or a tiger, or to struggle through a hidden swamp full of leeches.

Relaxing with copious draughts of beer, the men laughed and joked for it was not often they had visitors. 'It's an exciting life, all right,' said one.

'Yeah. Never know what's round the corner.'

'Child's play, really!' The tough sergeant wrenched off the top of a beer bottle with his teeth. It was presumably part of his rigorous training where men were taught to be resourceful.

Half an hour had passed without sign of the children and I was feeling uneasy. 'I wonder if we should look for them. They're rather accident-prone,' I said, with a feeble attempt at humour.

'I expect they're playing in the sand like most kids.' The rugged sergeant took a long swig from the bottle, relaxed and unconcerned.

---

1 basha: hut.

I was about to explain that our children were not like normal kids when I caught sight of them approaching. Michael was performing all sorts of strange antics, rolling on the ground, jumping up and down and shaking his head vigorously. He was adept at headstands and gymnastics but we felt embarrassed by this exhibitionism.

'What energy! He'd make a good Chindit,' remarked the Colonel, genuinely impressed.

'Looks as if he's finally taken leave of his senses,' said Charles sardonically. 'I hope he's looking after the girls.' I knew that he would reprimand Michael sternly afterwards.

The girls were following a short distance behind, also putting on a foolish display and shouting. But to my great relief they were safe, and I was prepared to overlook their misconduct. As they came closer, performing with increased vigour, I saw their faces and arms were covered in red blotches. They had inadvertently disturbed a wasps' nest, Michael having received the brunt of the attack. Our solicitous hosts, well-prepared for such a crisis, provided soothing applications of hamamelis,[1] which together with large infusions of sweets and chocolates, effected a complete recovery.

During the precarious days of the War, agitators who supported the Congress Party's civil disobedience movement had to be dealt with severely. When Gopal was arrested for inciting insurrection, his father, who was a *malguzar* of considerable standing, approached Charles to request pardon for his son.

Charles stood firm. 'Your son must be detained until the incident has been investigated,' he explained to the distraught man. 'I will review the matter when I return from my tour of the district in three weeks' time.'

After a fortnight on tour, our stores were running low and I compiled a list for the *dak-wallah*. Ever hopeful, I asked for biscuits, tinned fruit and other luxuries. The messenger's return was greeted

---

1 hamamelis: wych-hazel.

with eagerness and the provisions inspected carefully. As I dug into the sacks, I found not only a generous quantity of good quality rice, but biscuits, tinned fruit, condensed milk and even jam. Only when the bountiful sack delivered up toys for the children – a jigsaw puzzle, a dinky car, a pretty doll and more besides – did I become suspicious.

Charles interrogated the *dak-wallah*. 'Where did all these good things come from?'

'From the *malguzar*, Sahib. He is sending you gifts.'

On our return to Headquarters, Charles sent for the *malguzar*. 'Did you send me all those gifts while I was on tour?'

'Yes, indeed, Sahib. As a *nazar*,[1] Sahib. And there is more.' The *malguzar* salaamed deeply. 'My son, Sahib . . . when will you release him?' he asked eagerly.

Charles pointed out that there was a considerable difference between the customary and sanctioned *nazar* and a large gift given as a bribe. 'Did you not know that it is a serious offence to bribe an officer?'

British officers were forbidden to accept bribes and such cases were dealt with harshly. The *malguzar* was placed under arrest and the case came to Court a week later. The wealthy landowner could afford a good lawyer and the case was cleverly defended. Some lawyers had reputations for success, if not for integrity, and used all sorts of methods, including perjured witnesses, to get their clients off. It became evident that the *malguzar* was involved in the planned uprising together with his son. He was therefore sentenced to two years' imprisonment, not only for sedition but also for attempting to bribe a government officer.

It was the end of a busy day and Charles had not had time to read the mail. He glanced through the pile of letters, pinned together with a babul thorn,[2] to see if there was anything urgent. An incor-

---

1   *nazar*: token offered by an Indian to an official as a sign of respect and goodwill.
2   Many everyday items, like paper clips, were unobtainable during the War.

rectly addressed envelope attracted his attention and on opening it, he realized immediately that it was a code. A code was a challenge which he enjoyed and he decided to take it home.

Charles sat up late, trying to decipher the unintelligible letters and numbers.

'Can I help you?' I asked doubtfully.

'Well, two heads are better than one. I can't make much sense of it. My only clue is this symbol, which I've come across before . . . I think it stands for Congress. If so, this could be a subversive plot. The letter is certainly not intended for me.'

We bent over the bright pool of light from the hissing petromax lamp, puzzling over the incomprehensible message. 'One has to work on certain premises,' Charles explained. 'For example, we could presuppose that this symbol stands for Congress and this series of letters "xnwpfw", which crops up several times, stands for *Sirkar*.[1] In that case, we could put X for S, N for I, and so on, five letters forward in the alphabet. And these symbols may be place names . . . Bombay or Nagpur, perhaps. If this is some sort of subversive action against the Government, we must find out the place, date and time.'

Charles slowly pieced together the outline of a message. I was able to fill in a few gaps. A noisy dawn chorus was heralding the new day when he announced triumphantly, 'I think we've cracked it! I'll have to work fast if I'm going to stop this uprising. What time does the mail train arrive at Malapore?'

'From Bombay?'

'Yes.'

'About nine o'clock, I think. But why Malapore? Surely they would go to Nagpur?'

'I just have a hunch. Going straight to the capital is too risky. These people would know they are less likely to be apprehended at a small place. There are good road communications from Malapore and they can infiltrate easily, drumming up support as they go.'

'I see. That sounds very feasible.'

---

1 *Sirkar*: Government.

'I'll go and muster some men now and arrange for two buses. It's at least an hour by road to Malapore. We'll have to hurry.'

'Would you like something to eat?'

'No thanks. Just a cup of tea.'

Two police buses arrived at Malapore station shortly before the train pulled in. The group of twenty insurgents wearing Gandhi caps were easily recognisable and made no resistance. They were driven under escort to Nagpur, over a hundred miles away, for questioning.

'The ringleaders are dangerous men,' Charles told me later. 'They are in cahoots with others in Nagpur and elsewhere. It's all part of this movement to stir up trouble against the British. But most of them are cheerful rogues. They even thanked us for the comfortable journey to prison and the refreshments.'

'Did any of them deny their involvement?'

'Not at all. The only thing which puzzled them all was how we had discovered their movements.'

On the return journey from an outlying station during the rainy season, we were held up by a river in flood. The Vauxhall had often been towed across Irish bridges,[1] with water lapping at the doors, but on this occasion the surging torrent was too dangerous. We therefore retraced our route to a small station where we could spend the night.

On arrival we were warned about a thief who was on the loose, a clever rogue who had managed to evade the police for some time. With his escape cut off by the flood, it was unlikely that he would attempt a burglary that night. However, we took the precaution of unloading the car and putting our belongings into the duty room.

Charles and I spread our bedding rolls on the hard uncomfortable benches in the duty room while our constables shared accommodation with the local policemen in the adjoining dormitory.

---

1   Irish bridge: concrete low-level causeway, useable in dry weather only.

The Vauxhall crossing a flooded road.

'Damn mosquitoes!' Charles complained. 'I'm being eaten alive. It's amazing how they manage to get in despite the gauze screens.'

'I can't imagine how Indians get any sleep at all. Do they use nets?'

'Not as a rule. They usually cover their whole bodies with sheets and pull them up over their heads.'

'We'd better do the same,' I said, pulling the sheet over my head before I was pierced by another vicious needle.

After a restless night, we were woken at dawn by loud and angry voices in the adjacent room. 'I hope the argument hasn't been caused by our chaps,' said Charles irritably as he went to investigate.

'What's going on? We're trying to sleep.'

'Sahib, it is the *badmash*.[1] He is stealing things in the night,' explained the Head Constable in agitation.

---

1 *badmash*: bad man; rascal.

'Where? In the bazaar?'

'No, Sahib. Here, in this place.'

'You mean the *police station?*'

'Yes, Sahib.'

'How did he get in?'

'Through that window.' The constable sheepishly pointed to an open window. The gauze screen had been pushed up and the window was wide open.

'Has anybody tried to find him or look for clues?'

'Yes, Sahib. His footprints are clear in the wet ground. The *badmash* has escaped across the river.'

'The *river?* But he would surely be drowned!'

'The water has gone down. It is now possible to cross the river.'

'Well, he's certainly a clever rascal. What did he steal?'

'He took something from *each* of us, Sahib!' he exclaimed indignantly. '*Biri*[1] from one, Scissors[2] from another, matches . . . and *my* penknife.'

'And *nobody* heard him? Or felt anything? *Four* of you!'

'None of us heard or felt anything, Sahib.' All the cheated constables looked embarrassed. Charles was amused at the thought of the thief moving stealthily from one recumbent, head-shrouded policeman to the next. At least the audacious rascal had a sense of humour.

We laughed about the incident later. 'I can't blame the constables for not apprehending the thief,' said Charles. 'After all, the *chokidar*[3] didn't hear anything and neither did we. It goes to show that even the police can be caught napping sometimes!'

---

1 *biri*: hand-rolled tobacco leaf cigarette.
2 Scissors: cheap brand of cigarettes.
3 *chokidar*: night watchman.

The Special Armed Force (S.A.F.) on weapons training, instructed by the District Police Superintendent.

The Viceroy of India, Field Marshall Sir Archibald Wavell (left of centre), escorted by the Superintendent of Police (behind in uniform), during his visit to Jubbulpore (1944).

Chapter VI

Stranger than Fiction

By the faith of my tarnished soul,
All things I did not well
I had hoped to clear ere the fire died
And to lay me down by my master's side
To rule in Heaven his only bride,
While the others howl in Hell.
But I have felt the fire's breath,
And hard it is to die!

RUDYARD KIPLING 'The Last Suttee'

uman sacrifice is a part of Hinduism and is still practised in a clandestine way despite being ruled illegal by the British. Suttee, the ritual suicide of a widow on her husband's funeral pyre, is an honourable attempt to attain nirvana[1] by a final act of devotion and sacrifice. According to the Veda, the most ancient Hindu scriptures, suttee makes the dead man and his wife divine for it purifies their souls and frees them from the bondage of transmigration.

Suttee was not always voluntary as women were sometimes forcibly tied to the pyre or the corpse. The walls leading to the old Burning

---

1   nirvana: salvation or state of perfect peace, normally achieved after many reincarnations (transmigration). When the soul has been sufficiently purified, it can return to God.

Ghats of Jodhpur bear many small handprints of young Rajput widows, some mere teenagers, immolated with their heroic husbands who had died in battle. One imagines their terrified struggling and screaming as they were carried out to be burned. A rajah's prestige was often measured by the number of women who elected to throw themselves on his funeral pyre, the greatest honour being attributed to Ajit Singh in 1731, whose six wives and fifty-eight concubines shared his fate. Many a palace was said to be haunted by agonized screams of women being consumed in the pyre of a deceased rajah.

In times of crisis a sacrifice was sometimes made as an ultimate entreaty to the gods. The disappearance of a young girl in the district prompted a police investigation. It was said that she had been offered to the Goddess of Fertility in supplication for a good crop during the drought. The local *zemindar*, a man of considerable influence, was suspected but no-one would risk informing against him. Neither perpetrator nor victim could be traced but rumours arose to plague the common folk: the tree at the site of sacrifice had to be avoided lest its shadow struck one down, and for those who drank from the nearby river which was tainted with the victim's blood, death was inevitable.

A flock of vultures circling over a spot at the edge of the jungle attracted the attention of a farmer who was searching for a lost cow. He was amazed to find the scorched remains of a man under a pile of smouldering straw. Realizing it was not a normal funeral pyre, he reported the matter to the police.

The corpse was identified as that of a local forester, a well-known and high-caste Indian who commanded great respect. He had employed a large labour force and names of employees were still legible in a singed notebook. There was no shortage of informers, and the police soon established that on the day of his murder he had hired a bullock-cart in the bazaar where he recruited labour. He was known to carry large sums of money for wages and was therefore an obvious target for premeditated murder. A harnessed bullock-cart was found in the market and bloodstains on the cart were confirmed by the pathologist as human blood.

The Sub-Inspector, being possessed of 'infinite resource and sagacity,'[1] devised a simple plan. Accompanied by three independent witnesses, he drove the cart towards the jungle and gave the bullocks their heads. Anyone who has lived in India has seen trains of bullock-carts rattling along with their owners asleep, wrapped in blankets. At dusk, long processions of carts drawn by these patient beasts, nose to tail, wend their way home along familiar roads. Occasionally a wag has been known to turn one around so that when the unsuspecting driver awakes at dawn, he finds himself where he started the previous night. In this instance, the animals followed the road for several miles before turning on to a rough winding track skirting the jungle and leading to the very spot where the victim had been found. When confronted by this evidence, the owner of the bullock-cart confessed. The mute testimony of the bullocks could not be denied.

B hola Nath confessed that he had murdered his wife in a jealous rage because of her relationship with a neighbour. He explained that he had burned her body on a funeral pyre and he showed the site to the police. The self-confessed murderer was placed under arrest while the police tried to track down the neighbour, Bela Ram, who had disappeared. In the meantime, examination revealed that the charred bones were those of a goat, despite Bhola Nath's insistence that he had burned his wife's body. The cheated husband seemed unconcerned and relaxed in his prison cell. After all, he was well fed and was having a rest from his labours.

Some months later a report was received from an adjacent province about a suspicious couple from Rampur district who had been living in a *serai*[2] for several months. They were identified as Bela Ram and

---

1 Rudyard Kipling: *Just So Stories*.
2 *serai*: cheap accommodation for travellers; rest house.

the wife of Bhola Nath, and were taken back to their home town to account for themselves.

Bhola Nath was delighted to see his wife again. His explanation was simple: since he was a poor man unable to afford legal aid to trace his errant wife, his ruse had forced the police to take action at no expense to himself.

S*adhus* relinquish all worldly possessions and live solely on alms. They sometimes endure great hardship or practise bizarre and masochistic acts to show renunciation of the material world. They may lie on beds of nails or sit for years with outstretched arms which slowly wither away. Some are buried alive for weeks or are planted upside down with stick legs protruding like saplings. A man who was exhumed after the appointed time was still alive but partially eaten by ants. They are supported by the charity of pious Hindus and fed by their *chelas*.[1]

Holy men congregate at religious festivals where they are held in considerable awe, their ash-smeared bodies and matted dreadlocks giving them a sinister appearance. Brandishing tridents in obeisance to Lord Shiva,[2] they perform frenzied dances and torture themselves to 'entertain' the crowd and receive alms. We watched a man dancing wildly, foaming at the mouth as he flogged himself mercilessly. A group of *sadhus* piercing their cheeks, tongues and stomachs with long needles, did not flinch or show any sign of injury. Such incomprehensible demonstrations apparently achieve the final stage in the renunciation of their *karma*[3] and thereby give better status in the next world.

In Puri, religious fervour reaches a pitch during the spectacular Jagannath Festival. Jagannath is the incarnation of Krishna who, in

---

1 *chela*: disciple, pupil or servant.
2 Shiva: God of destruction, one of the supreme deities, symbolized by the cobra.
3 *karma*: existing state. Hindus believe a person's deeds in this and previous lives tally up to influence their status in the next.

turn, is the embodiment of the revered Vishnu, Preserver of the Universe. Effigies of the monstrous gaudy idol and his two siblings are taken with great ceremony from the magnificent temple and placed on three enormous chariots surmounted by brilliantly decorated canopies. Like mobile temples, these fifty feet high edifices are towed by thousands of enthusiasts through the vast crowd to the exuberant accompaniment of drums and cymbals. Delirious pilgrims cling to the beams and surge up the ramps on to the platforms trying to touch the gods. Inevitably, some get jolted off and are killed or trampled underfoot. Frenzied devotees attempt self-sacrifice to attain nirvana by flinging themselves beneath the enormous wheels. The police struggle to keep order and stretcher-bearers carry away the injured.

Hinduism and Islam are as incompatible as fire and water. The Hindus' worship of idols and their devotion to a pantheon of gods is anathema to the monotheistic Muslims who, not infrequently, desecrate Hindu temples adorned with deities. When a sacred cow was slaughtered outside a temple, the Hindus retaliated angrily by killing a pig outside the mosque. The ensuing riot had to be handled with extreme tact and patience by the police in order to defuse a very tense situation. The British adopted a policy of non-interference in religious matters; the police would mediate and try to keep the peace only when dissension led to strife.

During a Muslim festival, a march was planned along a road where a grand peepul tree was growing. Buddhists believe that Buddha received his enlightenment while meditating under a peepul tree and the trees have since been highly venerated. An angry deputation demanded that the route should be diverted lest the tall banners damage the branches. The crisis was averted by excavating a dip in the road so that the banners would not touch the overhanging branches, and the procession continued without offence to either party.

The early administrators in the 1830s saw the need for 'the recon-struction of a decomposed society'[1] and attempted to rectify the most glaring evils of suttee, female infanticide and human sacrifice. Hindu fanatics felt that making suttee illegal caused grave injustice by depriving human souls of the opportunity to free themselves from the bondage of transmigration. Generally, however, there was little hostility towards the administration and the Indians regarded the British as their protectors and their *ma-bap*.[2]

The British were fascinated and lured by India's munificence and her dazzling kaleidoscope of cultures, rituals and mythology, but the chasm between the cultures was too great to be bridged. Although the customs and attitudes of both changed over the course of time, the British and the Indians remained apart – incompatible, unassimi-lated and unreconciled. Rudyard Kipling expressed this sentiment in *The Ballad of the East and West*, written in 1892:

> Oh, East is East, and West is West, and never the twain
> shall meet,
> Till Earth and Sky stand presently at God's great
> Judgement Seat.

---

1 George Macaulay Trevelyan (English historian, 1876–1962).
2 *ma-bap*: mother and father.

Chapter VII

Domestic Hazards

As the heat mounted on the plains, the hill stations blossomed into vigorous life. Provincial headquarters were transferred to the nearest hill stations, and from March onwards, there was a steady migration of wives and children seeking refuge from the heat. This annual retreat to the hills was an indulgence which we could seldom afford. Instead, the torrid pre-monsoon heat was a challenge which had to be endured. We lived indoors, incarcerated in the gloomy, darkened bungalow, battling against lethargy and physical discomfort.

The first rays of sun struck like a searchlight, harsh and penetrating. Immediately, windows and shutters were closed to block out the heat and the glare. One did not venture outside unless absolutely necessary, and never without a topee. Indoors, *punkahs*[1] brought some relief until the *punkah-wallah* himself succumbed and fell into a stupor, his big toe attached to the pulling rope. Hira Lal would wake him up rudely, reminding him that he was greatly privileged to have the job as there was considerable competition for employment in the homes of officials.

The daily routine continued at a sluggish pace until the afternoon when the temperature reached a punishing one hundred and ten degrees in the shade. In the afternoon the entire household became

---

1 *punkah*: a fan suspended from the ceiling, usually made from palm leaves or coarse cloth. A *punkah-wallah* worked the fan to create a breeze by continually pulling a rope attached to it.

inert as though a spell had been cast. The *punkah-wallah* enjoyed a legitimate doze, unmolested by the bearer who had retired himself. The dogs lay spread-eagled on the wet floors in the open doorways where the breeze was cooled by the damp, sweet-smelling khus-khus tatties.[1]

There was an almost tangible feeling of relief at sundown as the heat began to abate. It was like coming to life again after being in Hades. One had a heightened awareness of the surroundings: the gentle golden twilight, the fragrant blossoms and the smell of wood-smoke drifting across the fields. It was the time to relax on the verandah with *burra-pegs* or long drinks with ice[2] if it was available, while the children expended their pent-up energy cavorting around. Our beds were placed on the gravel patio where the rough ground discouraged snakes and other unwelcome guests, while mosquito nets draped over wooden frames provided protection from winged intruders. It was often possible to read by the light of the moon and stars; only the howls of jackals and the barking of pariah dogs in the bazaar disturbed the peace. But it was not until the early hours that it was cool enough to sleep, a brief respite before the sun rose over the horizon and thrust us back into the furnace.

After many weeks of tormenting heat, a haze of exhaustion hovered everywhere. Tempers were frayed and people were plagued by headaches, prickly heat and blistering sunburn. The repetitive notes of the brain-fever bird and the barking of pariahs hammered relentlessly on one's taut nerves until one felt they would snap. It did not seem possible to bear any more tension and discomfort. At the beginning of June there was a great sense of expectancy as the monsoon approached, and much speculation as to the day of its arrival. If it broke a day or two earlier or later than usual, which in the Rampur district was the fifteenth of June, it was regarded as a freak season.

---

1 tatties: screens of khus-khus grass, doused in water to cool the breeze blowing through them.
2 Ice in large blocks could be bought from passing mail trains or from local factories, and was much sought after.

The monsoon was presaged by hot winds which whipped up spirals of dust and mercilessly lashed branches. Dark, suffocating clouds banked up and the air became saturated and sticky. Ominous rumbles of thunder came closer and blinding streaks of lightning cleaved the inky sky. Then a dramatic thunderous crack announced the deluge. Unbelievable quantities of rain drummed down with deafening intensity. It gushed from drains, overflowed from gutters and carved gullies in the hard bare ground.

One's tension was immediately relieved like the uncoiling of an overwound spring. People rushed out joyously, faces upturned, soaking in the heavenly bounty. Within days new life burst out and the parched earth turned green. But the joy and relief were short-lived. The torrential downpours soon devastated gardens and crops, cut off communications and turned dry nullahs into roaring torrents. Livestock and people were swept away by the swollen rivers and countless numbers, who at the best of times lived in poverty and squalor, were made homeless as their flimsy dwellings collapsed. Every year the monsoon took its toll with the drowning, famine and disease that followed in its wake. The pathetic survivors picked up the shreds of their lives and continued their wretched existences in the same threatening situations. Such crises were exacerbated during the War as the overstretched Government could not offer aid or compensation.

The outbreak of the rains caused a population explosion of insects. Unavoidable and unconquerable, they waged war, buzzing, biting and stinging at every turn. As a parting shot, a molested or crushed stink-bug[1] emitted a repugnant and persistent smell. Some invaders bored insidiously through books, clothes and wood, forming intricate tunnels and bringing about creeping destruction. At night the flying insects invaded: moths, beetles, mosquitoes, greenflies, and termites in frenzied nuptial flight. They hurled themselves against window panes and quickly discovered any access into the lighted interior. With suicidal mania they besieged lamps and jostled for space on the scorching glass. They crawled into beds, nestled in one's hair and

---

1 stink-bug: a small black beetle.

drowned in the soup on the dinner table. Piles of roasted insects were swept up each morning, flying ants[1] being gathered with particular care for they were a delicacy and a valuable source of oil to the Indians.

New leaks in the roof quickly became evident and any spare container was an important asset. We learned to judge with great accuracy where to place receptacles and the rates at which they filled, as it was important to know whether a jam jar or bathtub was needed to catch the night's inflow. Sometimes we misjudged or were taken off-guard by a new leak.

'I didn't sleep a wink last night,' Charles complained one morning. 'There's a new leak above my bed. A damn drop fell on my chest every ten minutes or so and woke me up whenever I dozed off.'

'Shall we contact the PWD?'[2] I asked doubtfully. The PWD, dilatory at the best of times, was hard-pressed to cope with the many problems caused by the rains.

'It's highly unlikely they'll do anything now. But perhaps they'll repair the roof before *next* year's rains.' In the meantime, we shifted the bed as far as possible from the offending leak and placed a mackintosh over his mosquito net.

Charles retired early the following evening hoping for a better night's rest. But the lullabies of the nocturnal choristers did not have a soporific effect. The high-pitched whine of mosquitoes and the chirring of crickets were accompanied by throaty monsoon toads. The bloated lovers continued to serenade tirelessly through the night, some venturing on to the verandah in search of tasty winged morsels. From time to time Charles, exhausted and irritable, leapt up and hurled them away.

As snakes, scorpions and centipedes were flooded out of their homes, they sought refuge indoors. Scorpions and spiders favoured the malodorous comfort of shoes. One soon learned the strange habits of one's room-mates and many a brush was avoided by shaking

---

1 flying ants: termites.
2 PWD: Public Works' Department, which attended to the maintenance of Government buildings.

them carefully from their lodgings. Snakes and centipedes preferred to nestle in cosy nooks or dark cupboards and could take one by surprise. Michael once shared an armchair with a krait, one of the most venomous Indian snakes. But having snuggled into a crease, it was lulled into inertness by the heat and its presence was fortunately unnoticed until later.

Each season had its inherent dangers and difficulties. The important thing was to anticipate the problems and be ready to deal with them.

A loud crash from the girls' bedroom sent me running to the scene to find Susan emerging from the folds of the heavy curtain that hung across the open doorway. The brackets supporting the rod had been wrenched from their sockets.

'The curtain fittings are not very strong,' I complained to Charles. 'Do you think we could ask the PWD to check them?'

'Actually, they are perfectly adequate for hanging curtains.' Charles was sometimes infuriatingly pragmatic. 'But they certainly won't stand up to the kids swinging on them.'

'Anyway, they are all too high for our curtains,' I objected. 'Perhaps we could get them adjusted. And while they're at it, the walls could be painted. After all, we're entitled to have the house redecorated.'

'You know what the PWD is like. But I'll do my best.'

By the time the PWD arrived a year later, we had adjusted the curtain fittings ourselves and the thought of the upheaval involved in redecorating the house filled me with dismay. The dirty walls were used with impunity by the children as writing boards and patches of damp had been decorated like abstract works of art. On a large patch roughly the shape of India, I had drawn a map with cities, rivers and mountains and I felt unreasonably irritated at the prospect of my useful teaching aid being obliterated. The overseer did not comprehend my argument or appreciate my art and he shook his head in disbelief when I asked him to leave that wall unpainted. It was soon covered by a mask of bilious yellow, the regulation colour for that year.

'All memsahibs are requesting this colour,' he informed me, regarding his handiwork with pride. 'We are making it specially on urgent demand from all and sundry.'

The cement floors, window-panes and furniture were soon peppered to match the walls. Even the yellow-speckled geckos seemed to look brighter.

The kitchen stood apart from the house, about twenty yards behind. A small room without windows, it was like a furnace with heat blazing from the wood fire of the brick *chula*. The building should have been condemned but until such time as the PWD attended to it, we had to manage. This was the favourite meeting place of the servants who were undeterred by the suffocating smoke and heat, and it was here that the *bobajee* or cook, Mohammed Ali, held sway.

Each year at the start of the rainy season, I provided two sturdy black umbrellas, one for the servants' personal use and one to protect the food on its passage to the bungalow. The domestic umbrella was in great demand by the numerous adherents of the kitchen and was not always available for its intended purpose. In fact, its unavailability probably accounted for the watery soup on many occasions. One year the overworked umbrella did not complete its required time-span, and Mohammed Ali produced the dejected remains, tattered fabric clinging to rusty spokes.

'As Memsahib can see, the umbrella is of no use. It is not protecting the food,' he said reproachfully.

'It hasn't lasted very long this year, Cook,' I rebuked him.

'Memsahib knows it has rained more heavily this year,' he countered.

The monsoon had certainly been heavier than usual and the rainy season was far from over. Unquestionably, a replacement was necessary. With resignation, I assented. After all, it was a small price to pay if the quality of the soup improved.

Alarmed shouts from the kitchen sent me hurrying to investigate. The *masalchee* rushed out of the kitchen closely followed by the *bobajee* with his turban askew and brandishing an axe. Probably a religious dispute or a personal insult, I surmised, for the cook would certainly not tolerate any disrespect from a mere assistant. Nevertheless, it seemed to be a somewhat violent and excessive reaction. With his passion so aroused, I knew my intervention would have no effect and I fervently hoped that the more agile *masalchee* would outrun the cook. Apparently they were hoping that Charles would resolve their disagreement for they dashed towards the office.

'Sahib! Sahib! *Maro!*'[1] they yelled in unison.

Charles, lulled into a doze by the hypnotic voice of the *munshi*[2] reading a report in the vernacular, was jolted awake. 'What's going on?' he enquired irritably as the panting men rushed unceremoniously into his office.

'*Burra sarnp! Burra sarnp!*'[3]

Leaping to his feet, Charles grabbed his shotgun which was always at hand for such emergencies, and followed the alarmists to the scene. By this time a crowd had gathered round the kitchen shouting warnings and advice to one another. Indians are prone to be dramatic and Mohammed Ali played the leading role impressively. The snake, he said, was the largest in living memory and had crawled towards him while he was lifting a huge saucepan of hot soup. At this point he digressed to describe the ingredients of the soup, for being in the noble service of the Sahib, it was his responsibility and his privilege to provide food of the finest quality against all odds.

---

1 *Maro!*: Kill!
2 *munshi*: secretary/clerk.
3 *Burra sarnp!*: Big snake!

'*Aré!* It was nearly the end of my life, but I saved the soup,' he proclaimed to his spellbound and admiring audience. Turning to the *masalchee* he asked, 'Was it not so?'

The *masalchee*, who had been listening attentively to this new and more exciting version of their narrow escape, nodded vigorously. He was more afraid of Mohammed Ali than of the snake since he was perpetually answerable to the cook, whereas the snake was merely a passing menace.

'Yes,' he agreed, 'he speaks the truth. But for the courage of Mohammed Ali, I would be dead!'

Meanwhile, alone in the kitchen, Charles was confronting the adversary. It took a few moments for his eyes to adjust to the gloom. Then he discerned a movement on top of the wall and saw the snake slithering into the thatch. He fired. The bisected body fell amid a pile of rubble from the disintegrating wall and a cloud of choking dust hung in the air for several minutes. Though not the monster boasted of by Mohammed Ali, the young four-foot cobra would have been dangerous if it had reappeared in the vicinity.

One's needs are answered in mysterious ways, I reflected. At last we had a good chance of getting a new kitchen.

O ur stocks of tinned and bottled provisions were running low and were unobtainable locally. At least I could make some jam as there was a prolific crop of *tiparris*.[1] I asked the *mali* to pick as many as possible while I prepared the equipment with uncharacteristic enthusiasm, for jam-making was not one of my skills. Gooseberry jam was a favourite of Charles and the children so I decided to make a large quantity, sufficient for the year and extra to give to friends. I knew that Mrs Pinto did not have *tiparris* in her garden and I felt pleased that I could reciprocate her frequent gifts of home-made preserves.

---

1   *tiparris*: gooseberries.

An hour later when I was beginning to wonder whether the *mali* had understood my instructions, he returned with a mere handful of berries. 'Where are all the *tiparris*?' I asked, puzzled and annoyed.

'Alas, Memsahib, the birds have eaten all. I have just caught this *badmash!*' Triumphantly he held up the remains of a crow. He shifted nervously and described an arc in the sand with his toes. 'Would Memsahib like some guavas instead?'

Clearly it had to be guava jam or nothing. 'All right. Get them as quickly as you can.' Soon he was back with a modest picking, enough for just a few bottles.

By then it was midday and the heat in the kitchen was stifling, but I was determined to persevere. I was compelled to use a *dekshi*[1] that was on the small side since the larger one was leaking, and the bubbling mass was dangerously near to the rim. It was not possible to regulate the heat on the simple *chula*; it was a matter of being on or off. I marvelled at Mohammed Ali and the culinary wonders he produced in such primitive conditions. Mrs Beeton's *Everyday Cookery* instructed, 'When the sugar has dissolved, boil rapidly without stirring.' I stood back and waited for a few moments. Suddenly, volcanic jets erupted in all directions, spattering the surroundings. Assiduously I applied the gelling tests as directed, noting with some anxiety that 'some fruits lose their setting quality if boiled too long and then the jam NEVER sets.' Despite my best efforts, the setting-point eluded me. The lava thickened and slowly solidified. I desperately hoped that no-one would appear on the scene and envied those housewives who could secretly dispose of their mistakes. I would certainly have to account for the fruit as the servants and children had eagerly been awaiting the outcome of my labour. Perhaps I could pass it off as toffee.

I heard Charles' cheerful whistle. 'What's cooking?'

'I'm making guava toffee,' I answered coldly.

---

1 *dekshi*: cooking pot.

'Toffee?' He sounded disappointed. 'Well, it's something different, I suppose, and the children will enjoy it. Are you going to make us some jam as well?'

George and Elspeth Simpson, like many missionaries in outlying areas, were qualified doctors.

One morning the woman who supplied their milk arrived with her sick child to seek medical help. The child had symptoms of an intestinal infection and needed prompt treatment. Elspeth pacified the distraught mother and gave her medication for the child. 'Has the baba been drinking unboiled water?' she enquired. Enteric disorders, including the often fatal diseases of cholera, typhoid and dysentery were usually caused by drinking contaminated water.

'She is drinking only milk, Memsahib,' said Sarifa. 'The same milk which I bring for Memsahib.'

'Then your baba should be all right,' said Elspeth comfortingly. 'She has a simple infection and it will be cured by this medicine.'

However, the little girl's condition deteriorated and for some days it was touch-and-go whether she would survive. Elspeth realized that it was dysentery after all and attended her carefully.

Eventually, the child recovered and Sarifa came to salaam the doctor. 'Memsahib, you have saved my baba's life!' she cried passionately, falling at Elspeth's feet.

'I am very happy for you, Sarifa.'

'Thank you, thank you, Memsahib. Never, never again will I water your milk!'

We became suspicious that the milk we were buying from the *gai-wallah*[1] was being watered and Charles checked its density with a lactometer. It had indeed been considerably diluted and the farmer was summoned.

---

1 *gai-wallah*: milkman.

'Would I, Chaman Lal, dare to put water in the milk?' The farmer was indignant. 'May *Khudah*[1] strike me dead if that is so!'

'You're lucky to be standing in that case!' said Charles sardonically. He demonstrated the lactometer test using both undiluted and watered samples.

In the face of the evidence, the *gai-wallah* was more humble. 'Sahib, my cows are old and their milk is thin.'

'But not *so* thin. This milk tastes of water.'

'There is no water in the milk, Sahib, only in the cream on top.'

The local laundry service was a family business. The *dhobi*[2] and his three sons had a large clientele including all the officials in Rampur. Not infrequently items of linen and garments strayed into other households but the majority of articles were eventually returned to their rightful owners, identified by characteristic markings. It was not unusual to exchange serviettes or children's socks at a tea party, or to discuss colour changes and other interesting developments resulting from the previous week's laundry.

The Dhobi

---

1   *Khudah*: God.
2   *dhobi*: washerman.

The clean laundry was usually delivered in the morning. The *dhobi* would stagger up the path with an enormous bundle slung over his shoulder and a smaller one containing uniforms and *jharans*[1] over his arm. It was hardly surprising that the poor man had a bowed back and bandy legs. Under Hira Lal's supervision, the clean linen and clothes were laid in neat piles on our beds. Then began the tedious business of checking. While I read the list, Hira Lal counted and examined the items. 'Seven pillow cases, eight sheets, two tablecloths, five towels.' All correct, fortunately, for linen was hard to replace. Then the clothes: 'Six shirts, two large, four small . . . four shorts, two large—' Hira Lal pounced on a pair of shorts and held them up for my inspection.

'Memsahib can see that the shorts of the Sahib are torn. Were they not as good as new when they went to be washed? This man is careless and washes badly.'

Such provocation could not be uncontested and a heated argument followed. The *dhobi*, stung by the aspersions, volubly defended his integrity and insisted that the damage had not been caused through neglect. Hira Lal proudly stood his ground for it was imperative that as the *khansama*, he should assert his authority over a mere *dhobi*. Eventually the *status quo* was restored and the checking continued.

'Ten handkerchiefs, nine *jharans*—'

'Where are the other two handkerchiefs and the other *jharan*?' I asked.

Hira Lal counted them again and smiled triumphantly. The *dhobi* shook his head sadly. 'Memsahib, why should it be that two misfortunes should occur together? Unhappy man that I am!'

'Well, what happened?'

'Memsahib, it is like this. Even as I hung out the washing in a safe place, down came a big *kauwa*[2] and took away two handkerchiefs. My sons and I pursued it unceasingly all day, but alas it was no good. As for the *jharan*—'

---

1 *jharan*: dusting cloth
2 *kauwa*: crow.

'Never mind!' The long babul thorns with which he had pinned the washing on the line had no doubt assisted in their demise. Well, two handkerchiefs and a duster were relatively dispensable and it was futile to pursue the enquiry. 'But what's happened to my blue dress, Dhobi?' I enquired in panic as I caught sight of a grey one among the folded garments. Changes in colour in the laundry were not an infrequent occurrence. But surely not my *new* dress, recently made by the *derzi*.

'What has happened to this dress?' I asked again, pointing to the discoloured garment in the pile of laundry and controlling my anger with an effort.

'Memsahib, it is as good as new.'

'But it was blue.'

'No, Memsahib, it was this colour.'

Fortunately for the *dhobi*, Hira Lal had retreated briefly to speak to a messenger and had missed the altercation, for he would certainly have taken the *dhobi* severely to task. He returned with a parcel and a note.

'Jameson Memsahib's messenger is waiting for a reply,' said Hira Lal.

Fuming about my ruined dress, I tore open the parcel and read the note impatiently. 'Oh, I see . . . Well, just ask the messenger to say thank you to Memsahib for the parcel with my blue dress. And please return this grey dress to Jameson Memsahib.'

Chapter VIII

As Good as a Rest

The railway station is part of the social framework of India and a microcosm of life. People converge from miles around and may wait for days for their trains. They set up makeshift lodgings on the platform by spreading *dhurries* and demarcating their territories with bundles, *bistras*[1] and trunks. Wicker baskets of squawking hens, tethered goats and restless children add to the confusion. Groups cluster companionably around braziers, passing hookahs, cooking rice and tossing chapattis, oblivious of the surrounding disorder. There is constant clamour and bustle as crowds press in all directions, picking their way around these camps and trying to avoid red blotches of expectorated betel, piles of goat dung, banana skins and litter. Raucous hawkers' cries rise above the general babel: '*Pahn biri!*[2] *Garum char!*[3] *Hindi pani, Mussulman pani!*'[4]

When we arrived at the station late in the evening, the platform was littered with sleeping bundles which sprang to life as the train drew in. Desperate people fought to get on and fought to get off, and turbaned porters with vast burdens forced their way through the crowd. The station master rudely thrust aside those who had been unable to gain entry and were clinging to the steps. With guilty relief

---

1   *bistras*: bedding rolls.
2   *pahn biri*: pahn leaf and cigarettes.
3   *garum char*: hot tea.
4   *Hindu pani, Mussulman pani*: Water for Hindus, water for Muslims.

we found our reserved compartment, our names surprisingly legible on the door.

A first-class compartment on the Bengal-Nagpur Mail was, by any standard, luxurious. The spacious, panelled, four-berth sleeper was cooled by an overhead fan and even had its own toilet closet and shower. Windows fitted with louvres and gauze screens offered some measure of privacy from the hawkers and beggars who thronged around at every station. A strong latch on the sliding door gave protection from unwanted bedfellows who might perch on the edge of one's bunk, as well as providing the security needed for a relatively good night's sleep.

We had decided to spend our ten days' casual leave in Bombay to renew our hazy acquaintance with Civilization. Fashionable shops, a smart hotel, cinemas and nightlife were exciting prospects to those who lived in backwaters. Michael would benefit from the experience but the girls would certainly find it overwhelming and exhausting, especially in the pre-monsoon heat, so we had arranged for them to stay with the long-suffering Monique, assisted by Ayah.

We dozed fitfully between stations, being rudely jolted awake each time the train came to a halt. Michael, curled up on the bottom of my bunk, slept with enviable ease. Two well-dressed passengers settled down on the opposite bunks in the early hours, but it was some time before we realised they were the Pundit Jawaharlal Nehru[1] and his sister, Kamala Nehru. At each station they were welcomed by enthusiastic supporters and presented with garlands and *pahn*.[2] Michael was soon bowed down with the excess garlands which Nehru smilingly placed round his neck. With commendable restraint, Charles confined his conversation to pleasantries such as the weather and the crops. In our unexpected role of travelling companions to the

---

1 Jawaharlal Nehru: Leader of the Congress Party who was campaigning for Independence and the end of British Rule. He became India's first Prime Minister after Independence in 1947. Pundit: a title of respect; an expert or teacher.
2 *pahn*: betel leaf, sometimes wrapped around parings of areca-nut and various additives.

respected Pundit, however, we enjoyed solicitous attention and when we arrived at Victoria Terminus in Bombay the following evening, Nehru cleared a passage through the large welcoming crowd and we swept through like celebrities.

The busy port of Bombay, the gateway to the West, is a thriving centre for trade from the exotic to the illicit. The diversity of races and traditions creates a flamboyant, cosmopolitan atmosphere. Nightlife in downtown Bombay caters for all tastes, from classic theatre and fashionable nightclubs to seamy haunts of the underworld. The city boasts more cinemas than anywhere else in the world, with billboards flaunting every conceivable film in a number of languages. One evening, anticipating some good clean fun, we opted for a talkie comedy at a classic old cinema. However, the fleas soon occupied all our attention as we sought relief by scratching and wriggling. The antics of the audience provided considerable amusement, but the film itself made little impression.

Summer was at its sizzling zenith and an incandescent haze hovered over the city making the skyscrapers shimmer. With the sticky heat at sunstroke-level, a hundred and twenty degrees in the shade, our cool apartment with gyrating overhead fan and a gentle breeze curling up from the sea, provided blessed relief. The palatial Taj Mahal Hotel in the throbbing heart of Bombay was an exhilarating experience – a taste of gracious living, a glimpse of the unattainable world of the affluent and a brief indulgence to be relished. Our elegant third-floor rooms had a spectacular view of the Gateway of India[1] and the Arabian Sea. As the sun sank in a golden sky, we relaxed with a feeling of complete well-being. Appetizing aromas wafted up from the kitchen, inviting us to dine. It was not often I had the opportunity to dress up and I was determined to rise to the occasion. I slipped on the slim-fitting crimson dress especially made by the *derzi*, Abdul Gaffar. It was simple and cool and, I hoped, suitably elegant. It drew one of Charles' rare compliments so that I felt elated

1 Gateway of India: a magnificent monument on the seashore, erected in 1911 to celebrate the visit of King George and Queen Mary.

as we set off for our meal. But as I stepped out of our apartment, a blast of hot moist air struck with cruel disregard for my carefully arranged coiffure and by the time I reached the dining-room, my face was damp with perspiration and my hair awry.

'Charles, do I look all right?' I asked anxiously.

'Well, perhaps not quite your best.' I could always count on Charles for the plain unvarnished truth. In an agony of embarrassment I slunk along behind the waiter, past *soignée* ladies, imagining their pity for a gauche countrywoman having her first taste of culture. My fashionable new dress had lost its allure against the dazzling spectacle of the immaculately groomed and jewelled beau monde.

'It's high time I had some new clothes!' I announced irritably as we settled down at the table, resplendent with silver and crystal.

'Clothes? What have clothes got to do with this? I thought you were hungry. This fish is delicious, I must say.' Charles, oblivious of my misery, concentrated on his second helping of pomfret, that delectable fish which is a speciality of the area.

The following morning we visited an exclusive boutique recommended by Monique. The couturière, Madame Stella, was said to design her own dresses so that her clients were assured of individuality.

We were fortunate to be the only out-of-season customers and received the undivided, if indifferent, attention of two languid Eurasian assistants. I am a craven shopper at the best of times, easily enticed and quickly intimidated. Charles, however, relaxed in an armchair and with the air of a connoisseur and tycoon, grandly demanded to be shown all the latest creations. Only the most exclusive, the most fashionable gowns would do.

The morning wore on and dress after dress was brought out for trial. 'Modom looks wonderful,' I was assured as I modelled each garment. But Charles was less enthusiastic, surveying me critically through a thickening smoke haze. None of the costly creations suited me, he said. They were unoriginal, unattractive, unflattering and overpriced. Honest and outspoken – though some might describe him differently – he could voice no approval. After a couple of hours of dressing and undressing, I was weary and dishevelled and prepared to accept almost anything. The assistants were utterly at a loss. Then Madame Stella entered with a flourish, plump arms outstretched and bracelets tinkling.

'Madame! Monsieur! Welcome to my leetle salon. Madame ees not yet satisfied? Camille! Lucille! Bring immediately zose beautifool new *modèles. Mon Dieu*, zose girls! So slow to comprehend. At one glance I see what ees right for Madame. Onlee ze best weel do!' From time to time Madame Stella included a few words of French – often inaccurate, for it was not her native tongue – to impress her English-speaking clients. We learned later that she was a Czech refugee, and she had only picked up French on arrival in Bombay a few years before.

Madame Stella flicked her heavily-ringed fingers at the assistants, who scurried off to unveil the latest exclusive models hidden from the common herd. Now things started to move. Charles, the worthy adversary, sat up with renewed interest and faced his sparring partner. I was clearly incidental. As I emerged from the cubicle in the latest Parisian model, an emerald-green silk with draped neckline and a generous bow, Madame was exuberant, no doubt excited by the prospect of making a sale at last. 'Ze dress looks *charmante! Mais charmante! N'est ce pas, Monsieur?*'

In answer to her question, Charles admitted reluctantly, 'It's not bad. A bit too long, though, and that thing around the neck spoils it. Would you take it off, please.'

Madame closed her eyes in exasperation, revealing eye shadow in a curious shade of purple that matched her voluminous pile of tinted hair. 'Eet ees no *problème, Monsieur*. Ze bow can be removed. But ze dress ees *un parfait* feet.' Then, for the first time noticing the person in the dress, she asked kindly, 'Madame ees *fatiguée?*'

'No, not at all,' I lied, and taking advantage of the sudden attention, said meekly, 'I think it makes me look too thin, don't you?'

'Too bony,' Charles agreed.

'Too bonnee? What means zat?'

'Like a skeleton,' Charles explained with his usual endearing frankness.

Madame raised her hands in horror. 'Eet ees not so! Madame so young, so sleem, so beautifool! Monsieur ees making a leetle joke, *n'est ce pas*? Only ze bust ees too small.' Retreating a couple of paces, she surveyed me professionally with purple-hooded eyes and said with a graphic gesture, 'You must leeft eet up . . . so! Zat makes z'appeel, you understand?'

It was clear that there was nothing Madame Stella did not know about busts. They could be shaped, or at least modified, to the dictates of fashion. This season busts were large and round, and should it be one's misfortune not to have been so endowed by nature, there were ways and means, Madame explained with a wink, to achieve those effects. She added comfortingly that next year the small bust could become stylish. I consoled myself that sooner or later I might become the envy of some; in the meantime I should accept my shortcoming with fortitude.

Revived and elated by Madame Stella's flattery, I obligingly tried on two more Paris creations, obviously made by the *derzi* in the back room where the familiar whirring sound of a Singer sewing machine could be heard. Charles was now taking an active interest, offering constructive advice to both couturière and model. Magnanimously, he decided that I should have all three designer gowns to which minor adjustments would be made to enhance my inadequate proportions.

I felt like a princess in the elegant green gown as we dined and danced the next evening. The following day I perused the hotel *dhobi*'s references carefully before sending it to be cleaned as I would take no risks with the exclusive and expensive garment. Within hours, the *dhobi* returned with a dull limp rag bearing little resemblance to my silk dress. In extreme agitation he explained that the shortage of benzine had necessitated the use of an alternative cleaning agent. Of course it was the War that was to blame and the hotel would pay compensation.

Madame Stella was *désolée*. Fortunately, she hadn't yet destroyed the pattern and she would make an exception by copying the exclusive designer garment. The *derzi* would put aside everything else to make it in record time for us, her very valued clients. And we could have a twenty-five per cent discount.

Mollified and deeply grateful, we arranged to collect the replacement a couple of days later. It was ready as promised and even Charles was impressed by the efficient service and reasonable terms.

'She's really quite a kind-hearted soul,' Charles conceded. 'It's good of her to give such a generous discount.'

When I tried it on later, it was as perfect as the original. 'It's a pity that one of the little buttons is missing,' I said.

'I'll pop down and ask Madame for one,' Charles offered obligingly. 'It's not far.'

In a short time he was back. 'That swindler!' he fumed. 'There's an identical 'exclusive designer' gown in her shop window – at half price!'

It was said that one could buy anything from a pin to an elephant in Crawford Market. Our diverse requirements included items for our friends in Rampur, who had compiled their shopping lists as soon as the news had leaked out that we were going to the City.

As we entered the sprawling labyrinth, we were greeted by a cacophony of shouts, squeals and thuds, and immediately engulfed by the swirling crowd. We looked at each other in dismay. 'Let's hurry up and get out of here,' Charles shouted irritably above the din.

Hastily I tore from my notebook a page of the simplest items and handed it to him. 'See you here in an hour,' I called as he strode off. Clutching Michael's hand firmly, I explored the nearby stalls in search of my banal requirements. Confronted by glittering silver and brass, aromatic spices and caged parrots, I would be lucky to find ordinary cooking utensils, underclothes and stationery.

Returning to our rendezvous an hour later with little accomplished, I wondered uneasily how Charles was coping. I looked around for somewhere to wait and noticed an unoccupied chair at the entrance to a small toyshop. The grinning shopkeeper, seeing that I had fallen for his bait, invited me to inspect his wares. Michael, who was showing a spark of interest for the first time that morning, was utterly crestfallen when I picked out a small naked celluloid doll, the cheapest item available. He protested vehemently, 'But Mummy, the girls don't play with dolls!'

'I'll explain later,' I shouted, as I claimed possession of the chair.

'Can't you get me a penknife instead?'

'It costs too much, Michael.'

'But—'

'I told you, I'll explain later.'

Fifteen minutes after the appointed meeting time, Michael asked anxiously, 'Do you think Daddy's lost?'

He voiced my thoughts, but instead I said, 'Don't be silly! Policemen don't get lost.'

From my vantage point I viewed the bargains displayed temptingly nearby. 'UNDIES ARE DOWN TODAY' boasted a lingerie stall where bright frilly knickers floated from the awning like Christmas decorations. 'BIRDS ON THE WING' were offered by the butcher in the adjacent stall where comatose fowls huddled unsuspectingly in wicker cages awaiting slaughter. Fly-adorned carcasses dangled from the rafters and scattered feathers created an effective setting.

The remonstrations of the toyshop owner indicated that another purchase was necessary in order to retain my chair. Should I risk Michael's scorn and buy another doll? Or a pair of celanese knickers being held up invitingly by the underwear merchant? '*Baksheesh?*' suggested the lingerie-specialist hopefully, pointing to his chair but the knickers, surrounded by a buzz of flies from the adjoining butcher's stall, held even less appeal than the cheap dolls.

Casting round for alternatives, I noticed an opulent moneylender, his enormous belly bulging over his *dhoti*, reclining on cushions behind security bars. From time to time he contemptuously threw a pie, an almost valueless coin, through the bars to a beggar or coolie. By this charitable deed he was presumably ensuring cheap entry into nirvana. He smiled amiably, offering to exchange rupees for pounds or dollars or francs – for a substantial commission, of course. He had plenty of everything, he said helpfully. But he had no chair, so I decided to keep my money just as it was. Michael, who had assumed an air of grave responsibility, watched me carefully and sighed with relief as the moneylender returned to counting his coins with sweaty fingers.

Having weighed up my options, I said at length, 'I might as well get another doll, one for each of the girls.'

'*No*, Mummy!' Michael said in desperation. 'You know that neither of them . . . but there's a cheap penknife . . .' His voice tailed off as he realized the futility of arguing with one who has lost her senses and he lapsed into preoccupied silence. From time to time he gave me an anxious, sidelong glance. I decided to restrain myself from buying any more cheap toys even if it meant relinquishing my seat, and absorbed myself in watching the slow-moving circus: vendors and beggars, coolies balancing produce on their heads, chickens running riot, pi-dogs slinking around in search of scraps, goats with tinkling bells. Suddenly, in the wake of a lumbering cow and a procession of women collecting cow pats,[1] appeared Charles, dishevelled and harassed.

'Did you get lost, Dad?' Michael could not conceal his relief.

'Of course not! Where on earth have you two been? I've been looking for you everywhere.'

'We've been waiting here for ages . . . I had to buy dolls to secure—'

'*Dolls*? Who for? But surely the girls—'

Charles and Michael exchanged bewildered glances. 'I'll explain later,' I said hastily. 'How did you get on with the shopping?'

Charles thrust the torn page at me. 'What are -ocks and -ooks?' he asked aggrievedly.

'Oh, those are socks for Michael and yourself, and books for us all,' I laughed.

---

1   cow dung is valuable for fuel and for plastering walls and floors.

'Well, really, Brenda! How was I supposed to understand your hieroglyphics? I've bought two padlocks and some hooks instead. Anyway, they're always useful. Come on, let's get out of here! Oh, by the way,' he called over his shoulder as he elbowed a passage through the throng, 'I also bought a penknife for Michael.'

Bombay's glittering facade with its spacious boulevards and grand Victorian-Gothic buildings belies the wretchedness of the majority of its inhabitants. Countless numbers live in squalor and eke out a hand-to-mouth existence by begging or selling on the streets. Craftsmen living in tiny hovels in the utmost discomfort, painstakingly create luxurious articles to please the rich. They learn their craft as children and spend their whole lives at it. Weavers produce exquisite gossamer silks and elaborately woven rugs; metal workers fashion silver and brass into delicate filigree; carvers create intricate articles, taking days over a single item. The high-street shopper conjures up false ideas of wealthy merchants, knowing nothing of the stringent conditions under which they work. Shops well-stocked with tropical treats and smart restaurants serving sumptuous feasts spuriously suggest a plethora. Among the palatial residences of Malabar Hill, the Parsees'[1] macabre Towers of Silence loom incongruously, a sober reminder of the fate that awaits all. Corpses are left on open platforms on the towers for vultures to pick clean, thereby avoiding pollution of the sacred elements. These eerie towers remind one that the rich and poor will come to the same end; that the deprived and suffering may attain their nirvana more easily than the affluent and the pleasure-seekers.

---

1   The Parsees are a distinguished and cultured sect, centred in Bombay. They are descendants of the Persians who fled to India from Muslim persecution in the seventh and eighth centuries.

The train rattled across the dun-coloured plain scored by waterless river-beds and dotted with patches of withering crops which would provide grudging yields. Villages of mud huts, tenuous human habitations indistinguishable from one another, appeared and receded. The sun glared from a grey sky, dulled by a canopy of dust. We were prepared as well as possible for the tedious and oppressive journey home across the plains: a large block of ice in a tin tray on the floor to alleviate the sticky heat, thermos flasks of iced water, juicy fruit, and those rare luxuries from the city – relatively up-to-date copies of *The Statesman* and *The Times of India*.

At every station the train was besieged by wailing processions of beggars and vendors. At Deolali, an army depot, we were attracted to the window by the sweet singing of a young Indian girl. She danced as she sang in a strong mid-Western accent, *'Pistol Packin' Mama, lay that pistol down'*. It was a clever ploy and she was well-rewarded by the passengers, but her takings would be shared by the ravenous multitude. Begging is a way of life in India: an unfortunate practice which was abetted by the misguided generosity of American and British troops.

When a train drew out of a station thieves often boarded the dark off-side to prey upon sleeping and unsuspecting travellers. Having obtained their booty, they would leap off at a bridge or level-crossing as the train reduced speed. Since there were no corridors, the dining-car had to be boarded at a station and left at the next. Careful planning was necessary if one wanted a meal without undue risk to one's children or belongings. Before making our way down the platform to the dining-car at Deolali station, we closed the windows and screens of our compartment and instructed Hira Lal and Michael to lock the door and to pull the emergency cord in the event of a crisis. The alarm cord dangled within easy reach like a lifeline, but considerable strength was required to pull it and persistent effort was needed to alert the dilatory guard. Experienced travellers did not therefore have sanguine expectations of assistance in emergencies. An armed intruder would either have maimed his opponent or effected an escape by the time help arrived.

In the early hours we were woken by incessant beating on the windows. The train ground to a halt as a seething mass of locusts, an inestimable number, barred the track and blotted out the light. The frenzied flight would eventually descend to earth and the creeping carpet would devour every leaf in the line of its march. Swarms frequently annihilate whole crops, causing widespread famine and misery. Only the fallen bodies of the insects, harvested and feasted upon by the locals, bring any benefit. Locust plagues are just one of the scourges that regularly bedevil India. In this vast and overcrowded land, disaster is common and life is pitifully cheap.

Chapter IX

The Fakir's Grave

usk was falling as we rattled along the eroded drive to the dak-bungalow. Forlorn and neglected in a wilderness of high grass and lantana, it was far from inviting to the weary traveller.

'We'll have to stop here, I'm afraid,' Charles said with resignation.

'Oh, no! It's awful, Charles. Let's continue to the next bungalow. It can't be more than twenty miles.'

'More like forty. I'm exhausted, aren't you? Anyway, it's just a bed for the night.'

I felt apprehensive and uneasy. With the disintegrating thatch and mud-bespattered walls under tangled bougainvillaea, the bungalow was eerie and forbidding. 'There's something funny about this place. It makes me nervous.'

'There's nothing to worry about. It's just a bit gloomy and uncared for. Not used much, I expect, and the *khansama* has got a bit slack.' Charles stopped the engine, gave several sharp blasts on the hooter and eased his way out of the driver's seat, followed by Kim, the terrier; at least we described him euphemistically as a terrier, his origins being rather obscure. However, what he lacked in noble lineage, he more than made up for in courage and we would not have changed him for any prizewinner at Crufts.

Hira Lal and Kisnia seemed to share my reluctance and remained in the car. 'Come on! Get going!' ordered Charles. 'Where the devil's the *khansama*? Tell him to open up the place and lay on some hot water for baths.'

The slanting rays of the setting sun caught one of the windows and were reflected like two malignant red eyes growing more hooded each moment. If we had to spend the night here, I decided, it would certainly not be in *that* room with the eyes.

'Oh, please can't we go on?' I pleaded. 'It's not too late.'

But Charles was adamant. It had been a long day and the next would also be busy. 'We can relax on the verandah later, darling, and watch the sunset,' he said encouragingly. 'It's a lovely evening.'

In the small living-room the drab utilitarian furniture was covered in dust and festooned with spiders' webs whose occupants were plump from a surfeit of mosquitoes. Numerous geckos presumably accounted for many others but judging from the incessant buzzing, there were plenty of survivors. To my dismay there was only one bedroom – the room with the red eyes – made more obnoxious by a flourishing growth of mould on the walls and a foul stench of bat droppings and other odours. Undoubtedly there was also a healthy population of rats.

Later, as we relaxed with drinks on the verandah we watched the deepening twilight clothe the distant hills in a gentle rosy mantle. It was very soothing and I felt my apprehension melting away.

Kisnia appeared with a timid little man in a *dhoti* and over-sized turban. 'This is the *khansama*, Ram Das,' he explained as the man salaamed deeply. 'He lives in the village a mile away and not in the quarters here. The sweeper also lives in the village.'

'Why don't you live here and do the work you are paid for by the *Sirkar*?'[1] questioned Charles.

'Speak and do not tell lies!' commanded Kisnia sternly.

The man hesitated, clearly distressed. 'The Sahib does not like to be kept waiting,' prodded the orderly impatiently.

Ram Das sighed. 'Sahib, you are my mother and my father and when I am called, I am coming. Twice a month I am cleaning the

---

1 *Sirkar*: Government.

bungalow and the *mehtar* is sweeping the floors. But it is a year since any sahib stayed here. The quarters are clean and the rain is not falling through the roof. Sahib, I am a poor man and but for the money which the *Sirkar* pays, my family would surely be starving. But I cannot do the work if I am living here.'

'Why can't you live here?'

Ram Das salaamed again, bending almost double in an effort to prove his sincerity. 'Hazur, this place is bad. There lies a curse on it. It is not good to spend the night under this roof. If I am lying, may *Khudah* cut off my tongue and strike me dead!'

'Now explain clearly and do not speak in riddles,' Charles ordered, signalling to Kisnia not to interrupt.

The *khansama* pointed a trembling hand towards a large mound about thirty yards away in the corner of the compound. A paraffin lantern, partly concealed by grass and weeds, flickered on the mound. 'There, Sahib! There lies the grave of the *fakir*. It is well known that his spirit is walking. It is not safe to remain here when day is done.'

Charles, always logical and pragmatic, found it difficult to curb his impatience. 'What happens to those who stay?'

Ram Das shifted uneasily, his eyes resting fearfully on the mysterious mound. 'Many strange things, Sahib. He who spends a night here is having no peace. It could be worse . . . And there is an animal that is looking like a dog . . .' His voice trailed off and he coughed nervously.

'Enough of this nonsense! Go and make preparations for dinner and see that the rooms are clean.'

'*Gee haan*, Sahib,' Ram Das replied meekly. Even the ebullient Kisnia, inclined by virtue of his status to hector lesser mortals, was subdued.

I could hardly restrain my curiosity until they had departed. 'What do you think he was going to say about the animal that looks like a dog?'

Charles was non-committal. He stubbed out his cigarette and poured himself another drink. 'He must have seen a jackal or something – plenty of them around. He's linking it with the *fakir* for some reason. You know what imaginations these fellows have. I've yet to meet an Indian who isn't superstitious.'

'But surely there's more to it than that,' I persisted. 'He was genuinely scared.' I shivered, pondering the implications of Ram Das' words.

'For Heaven's sake, don't take this seriously.' But I sensed that Charles was also uneasy and knew more than he cared to admit for there was little that the police did not know. 'Why let this nonsense spoil our evening, darling?' He spoke with feigned cheerfulness, hedging.

The lamps had been lit and it was time to go inside. Charles had to attend to urgent dispatches and I needed to make out orders and write letters. But the paperwork had to be abandoned as both our petromax lamps, normally so reliable, faded and would not respond to pumping or coaxing with new mantles. With a last upsurge and splutter, one was finally extinguished while the other flickered feebly. The bungalow's dull lamps, quite inadequate for writing, were at least appreciated by the insects which competed for space on the hot glass, intent on self-immolation.

Hira Lal, who was a stickler for etiquette and considered no meal for the Sahib's table adequate without at least four courses, had prevailed upon Ram Das to produce his best. Accordingly, within a surprisingly short time, Ram Das had prepared a relative feast starting with clear soup, well-watered but enhanced with sippets. This was followed by fried murrel, a delicious freshwater fish that had been presented to Charles by a local *zemindar*. The main course of roast chicken, a tough old bird of doubtful origin, was served with the inevitable lady's fingers. The meal was rounded off with stringy local apricots, obviously a good standby for infrequent guests.

In the meantime the bedroom had been roughly cleaned though the musty smell persisted. The lumpy coir mattresses, disguised by our own clean bedding and veiled with mosquito nets, looked almost inviting.

'*Gosul ki pani lao*,'[1] Hira Lal shouted into the darkness. After hot baths in the tin tub, we climbed gratefully into bed and fell asleep almost immediately. Kim was curled up contentedly on his blanket beside us. But it seemed to be only minutes before we were awakened by his low growl and Hira Lal's discreet coughing on the other side of the curtain. Charles, roused from a deep sleep, reacted sharply.

'What do you want?'

Hira Lal coughed again apologetically. 'If Sahib permits, Kisnia and I will sleep in the living-room.'

'Why? What's the matter?'

'We do not know what might happen, Sahib, and are much afraid.'

'Well, sleep where you wish, but don't disturb us again!'

It was nearly midnight when we were awoken again, this time by a chorus of animals. It was a normal nocturnal occurrence but one I had never become accustomed to: hysterical giggling of hyenas, the eerie banshee-like call of a *phiaou* answered by the high-pitched yelling of the jackal pack, a wild dog baying at the moon. The blood-chilling cacophony was so close and penetrating that we felt surrounded by the beasts.

'I'll fix them!' muttered Charles. He pulled on his dressing-gown and groped for his slippers which he had placed on the bedside table out of reach of scorpions. The torch was dead, the batteries flattened by damp, and the dim petromax was the only available light. Uncertainly, I followed Charles who was feeling his way outside.

'Watch your step,' he warned, 'I nearly trod on a scorpion!'

Kisnia and Hira Lal rose hastily from their mattresses in the living-room and followed us out to the verandah. The rain clouds had cleared and the pale light of the waning moon cast dark shadows. On the *fakir*'s grave the lantern glowed a ghostly yellow. The maniacal howls rose to a crescendo and Kim, who had been growling softly, suddenly broke into a dismal yowl. Hackles up and ears laid back, he was clearly afraid.

'It's all right, Kim,' I soothed, though I felt far from calm.

---

1 '*Gosul ki pani lao*': 'Bring the bath water.'

An animal like a large dog or jackal, only thirty yards away and clearly visible in the moonlight, loped unhurriedly across the open space towards the grave, stopping in the shadow of a bush. Charles raised his shotgun. As he drew a bead on the target he was distracted by a commotion from Hira Lal and Kisnia who had been cowering behind.

'Sahib, Sahib! Do not shoot!' Hira Lal implored, his teeth chattering with terror. 'It is not an animal but a *bhoot!*'[1]

Kisnia wrung his hands in despair. 'Hazur, it is as the *khansama* said. Before the *fakir* himself appears he is preceded by a dog.'

'Nonsense!' Charles said roughly. 'Do you not know that to a Mussulman a dog is unclean? Why then should he choose a dog to precede him?'

Hira Lal, normally polite and deferential, was emboldened by fear. 'That is so, Sahib, but I beg you, don't shoot. Evil may befall us!'

Charles was in no mood for argument. 'We'll see! I've had enough of this, I'll get the damn thing if I have to stay here all night. Besides, a shot will frighten off other animals.' Then, as the brown slinking form appeared briefly from the shadow, he fired. An uncanny silence followed. There was no yelp or whine, no wounded animal limping away.

'Must have dropped in its tracks,' said Charles. 'We'll have a look in the morning. Now let's get some sleep. Come on Kim.' But Kim had already retreated to the refuge of his basket. Hira Lal and Kisnia had crept back to the living-room and were wrapped in their blankets, silent and trembling. They did not wish to be associated with Charles' rash act or be affected by the curses and recriminations which would surely emanate from it.

A light wind had sprung up causing the lantern to splutter. The high grass whispered a curious susurration and a babul thorn scraped the roof rhythmically as if tapping out a secret message. Somewhere in the distance an owl hooted. If a witch had ridden past on a broomstick I would not have been surprised. Glancing towards the

---

1 *bhoot*: ghost.

fakir's grave I noticed the lantern had gone out. It was hardly surprising with the mounting breeze. Or it could be that the paraffin had run out. Whatever the reason it would certainly be construed as a sign of displeasure from the long-dead holy man whose peace had been disturbed.

After that, both Charles and I dozed fitfully. I was haunted by ghosts and pursued by monsters. I awoke with a pounding heart as a hideous beast with grizzled beard, giggling insanely, lunged at me. When I eventually dared to open my eyes, I stifled a scream as the shadow of a grotesque creature raced across the ceiling.

'Rats!' said a grim voice next to me. 'One of the brutes landed on my mosquito net just now through a hole in the roof.'

'Oh, Charles,' I whispered, as reality dawned and I saw another hugely magnified and distorted shadow streak across the ceiling, 'I'm so scared!'

'It's all right, darling,' Charles said soothingly. 'They can't hurt you.'

Kim, his courage restored by something tangible, raced excitedly round the room in pursuit of rats. Judging by the squeals, he savaged several or at least rendered them motionless. The illuminated hands of my clock pointed to a quarter past three. Perhaps we could snatch a couple more hours sleep before dawn . . . But even as I was considering this, frenzied howling broke out afresh from the direction of the grave. 'Hyenas around the carcass, I expect,' said Charles. I shuddered as I visualized the ghoulish scavengers and the gory remains with the bones already picked clean.

Sleep was now out of the question. Red-eyed with weariness, we decided to leave even earlier than planned, keen to get away. Hira Lal and Kisnia, troubled and subdued, needed no urging to pack the paraphernalia. Charles and I brushed our way through the tall grass to the spot where the carcass would surely be lying. Charles was a good shot and the target had been within easy range so there was little doubt that he had killed it. The victim must have dropped close by and there would be traces of it. But there was *nothing*. No blood, no bones, no spoor, not even flattened grass. It was as if the incident had never happened.

Puzzled and disconcerted, we returned to the bungalow to find the car already loaded and Kim ensconced in his usual place on the back seat. Normally exuberant and eager for an early morning walk, he conveyed his reticence with pleading eyes and an apologetic wag of the tail. Nearby, Hira Lal, Kisnia and the *khansama* talked gravely in low voices. No doubt they were relieved that Charles had missed his target.

Thankfully, we rattled down the potholed drive. As we turned out of the rusty gate, I glanced back at the mound which had been the cause of so much trouble during our brief visit. A dust-devil,[1] a not uncommon occurrence, was whirling over it. Surprisingly, the lantern on the grave was glowing dimly despite the wind. Who had had the temerity to relight it?

Charles would say I was imagining it, just as he would explain away all the happenings of the previous night. In the reassuring light of day most things could be given a rational explanation: Kim's very real terror, the fear of the servants, the recalcitrant paraffin lamps, the slinking animal which had escaped the bullet . . . A logical and phlegmatic person like Charles would account for all these.

I remembered Ram Das' words, spoken with such feeling: 'He who spends a night here has no peace.' Well, thank goodness we would never return. The *fakir* was welcome to his claim and few would dispute it.

'There's only one thing that's certain,' remarked Charles, as though he had read my thoughts. 'It was the most restless and unpleasant night I've spent anywhere. A succession of silly incidents.'

'Well, not so silly. Quite real and frightening.'

'You're almost as superstitious as the Indians,' he teased.

For a long time I was disturbed by memories of that strange, inexplicable incident. When I heard that the dak-bungalow had

---

1   dust devil: whirlwind. This would be construed as an evil omen or indicate the presence of an evil spirit.

burned down a year later, I had an intense feeling of relief. 'I'm not at all surprised,' I commented. 'That paraffin lamp among the tinder-dry grass was asking for trouble.'

'It wasn't the lantern that caused the fire.'

'Then how did it happen? Was the *fakir* up to his tricks again?'

'We don't know for certain how it started. But reports say it was struck by lightning during the monsoon.'

'Well, I'm glad it's all over and done with,' I sighed, remembering the evil atmosphere of the place.

'On the contrary, I'm afraid. The mystery deepens!'

'What do you mean?'

'You see, the so-called lightning was probably a bolt of paraffin-soaked cloth—'

'You mean it was purposely burned down? Who was responsible?'

'We strongly suspect the local *zemindar*, a man called Piari Lal, although we can't prove it.'

'The man who gave us that tasty murrel?'

'Yes.'

'But, why *him*? You could understand the *khansama* or the sweeper doing it, but why the *zemindar*?'

'Well, the PWD decided to do the place up again, but Piari Lal resented the idea because he looked on the compound as his own. He had used it for many years to grow crops and graze cattle. The well supplied his water and so on. When the PWD started work on the place, he wanted to protect what he considered his own preserves. So he probably burned it down, assuming that the bungalow wouldn't be rebuilt for some time. He's been arrested for interfering with government property.'

'What about the *fakir*'s grave? Do you think it's a hoax?'

'Oh, no. The mystery surrounding the grave is well known. It's been in police records for years. The *khansama* and the sweeper were genuinely frightened. Piari Lal is an astute chap and played on their superstitious fears for his own ends so that few ventured near the place.'

'So you've known about it all the time. Why didn't you tell me when we were there? I wasn't imagining things after all.' I felt upset and resentful.

'I didn't tell you at the time because I knew you would be worried and frightened.'

'What about those two unfortunate servants? Have they lost their jobs?'

'Well, the sweeper resigned voluntarily, but the *khansama* died.'

'*Died*? How?'

'I'm not sure. He was found dead in the compound one night after the fire. The post-mortem reported death by natural causes.'

I was shocked. 'But he was quite young. And in any case, what was he doing there if he was so terrified of the place?'

'He'd been given an ultimatum by the PWD. He either had to live on the premises or lose his job. He had little alternative with a large family to support. The poor fellow probably died of sheer fright.'

'So we're none the wiser after all,' I said, disconcerted. 'The *fakir* is still in control.'

Chapter X

Odds and Ends

L ike many missionaries, Hiram and Cornelia Bemberger had devoted their lives to spreading the Christian Gospel among Asians. They had lived for many years in Shahpur, an isolated up-country station where they had established a flourishing Christian community.

When we arrived in the district after a hot and dusty journey, Susan had a raging temperature and we were advised to take her to Hiram who was a doctor. 'I'll do orl I can with the dear Lord's help,' Hiram assured us, as he gently led the whining and protesting child to his small outdoor clinic.

Cornelia was concerned to hear that we were camping. 'Now I reckon you stay right here with us,' she said magnanimously, unperturbed by our number. 'Ayah and the bearer too, of course. Hiram's Helpers in the Field have gone on furlough back home to Kansas and their rooms are vacant. Besides, it's real good to see other folks now and again.'

We didn't need much urging as we were tired and anxious about Susan, and the thought of comfortable beds in lieu of stretchers, was irresistible. While Charles and Hira Lal returned to the campsite to pack up, Cornelia gave me a guided tour of the absent tenants' rooms. Anxious and tired though I was, I endured with a creditable show of interest her running commentary on the battered furniture and chipped china ornaments. Most of it had apparently survived an arduous journey on the *Mayflower* with the Pilgrims.

'This lil' ole rockin' chair,' she said, lovingly stroking the dilapidated piece, 'belonged to Louisa-May's English grandmother – a kinda family heirloom, I guess.'

'It must be very valuable. Perhaps we should put it out of reach of the children. You know what kids are like.' I visualized them rocking vigorously as soon as my back was turned.

Cornelia beamed. 'Such dear children. So well-behaved. They wouldn't do anythin' wrong, Honey.' She certainly had remarkable, if misguided, faith in children and I hoped that my offspring would not be the ones to disillusion her.

Later, Charles, exhausted by the long drive, flung himself on the rickety chair so that it creaked and rocked violently. 'For Heaven's sake, that's a priceless antique. It's not meant to be sat on!' I exclaimed anxiously.

'Well how on earth should I know?' Charles was indignant. 'It looks fit for the scrap heap!'

'It travelled on the *Mayflower*,' I laughed.

The children were warned firmly not to touch any of the treasures. When Michael stole a quick ride on the forbidden rocker, the creaking of the ancient timber immediately drew our attention. He was sternly reprimanded with the result that he avoided a similar rocking chair in the drawing-room. 'Orl the children who come here love that chair,' said Cornelia. 'Wouldn't you like to sit in it, Michael?'

'No thank you,' answered Michael, the picture of propriety. 'I don't like rocking chairs.' Cornelia shook her head in amazement and Charles and I exchanged amused glances.

'When I was a boy,' said Hiram encouragingly, 'we had a lil' ole rockin' chair on the porch and my brothers and I would just rock 'n rock. Well, I guess we weren't as well-behaved as these dear children.'

Hiram and Cornelia were delighted to meet Ayah who was an ardent Christian.

'You're fortunate to have Sister Kumari in your family circle. She's such a lovely Christian,' Cornelia commented as we sat down to the evening meal.

'Sister *who?*' asked Charles.

'*Ayah!*' I whispered. Michael and Judy giggled at Ayah's sudden transformation while Cornelia, misinterpreting their amusement, smiled at them affectionately.

We were all hungry and were looking forward to something different to the usual camp fare, something typically American; Chicken Maryland and apple pie, perhaps. As we waited for the food to be served, the children bit into the crusty home-made bread placed invitingly on the side plates. Cornelia coughed politely, drawing us all to attention. 'Now Mr Bemberger will call a short blessing before we break bread.'

During Hiram's prolonged blessing the children continued to munch, happily oblivious of the solemnity of the occasion, and I realized guiltily that I had failed to teach them this simple social grace. I mused on the possibility of giving them some religious education while we were in the right setting. Ayah would also welcome the chance to talk to them about godly virtues, as indeed she had tried to do many times in the past without much success.

'Thanks be!' pronounced Hiram in conclusion, bringing me back with a start. I noticed that the children had finished their bread during the grace and were looking round hopefully for more. The mere thought of the Chicken Maryland was mouth-watering. With difficulty I concealed my disappointment as pumpkin pie and corn fritters were borne in.

For Ayah, the proximity of the church in Shahpur was a divine gift. She needed little encouragement to give religious instruction, and the heady sound of church bells provided the perfect setting. The following morning Michael and Judy were cajoled into joining a group of eager mission children whom Ayah had assembled under a shady tree. In order to prevent disruption from the unwilling attendees, I sat in the background with the convalescent Susan propped up on a chair.

Ayah had been brought up in an Anglican mission in Orissa. Her most treasured possessions were a Bible, and a simplified though fearsomely illustrated book of Old Testament stories in Hindi, which had been a parting gift from the deaconess. She knew these tales off by heart, and embroidered by flights of fancy, recounted them to the children from time to time. Her taste was inclined towards the macabre and she would dwell on the gory details: the beheading of John the Baptist, Abraham about to slay his son, Elisha calling out the bears to attack the children, and so on.

Ayah began her bracing recital in Hindi in time-honoured fashion. 'Once there was an old man whose name was Ibrahim who had a son whose name was Ishaak—' The mission children listened spellbound; Michael, Susan and Judy were bored as they had heard it all before, but were waiting for the climax where Abraham binds Isaac and produces a knife.

Michael was scornful. 'Why didn't Isaac run away? I would have done.'

Unfortunately, the story had a disappointing ending with Isaac escaping unscathed. For some unaccountable reason my children did not like stories that ended happily. 'Tell us about John the Baptist,' asked Michael. This was a hot favourite: the real thing with blood and lust and a rolling head.

Flattered by the enthusiasm, Ayah obliged. 'Now there was a big rajah called Herod who had lots of rupees and many *rajbaris*[1] and plenty of servants . . .' The children waited impatiently for the decapitation. At this point they began to heckle.

'Did they cut off his head with a knife or an axe?' enquired Michael.

'Did they sharpen it first?' asked Susan, roused from her sick-bed.

'Was there a lot of blood?' Judy always paid attention to details.

Arébaprébap!' exclaimed Ayah despairingly. 'What unnatural children are these! How do I know these things? I have told you what is

---

1   *rajbaris*: palaces.

in the book.' But the children clamoured for answers, refusing to be done out of the gruesome details.

'Be quiet!' I commanded my trio sternly. 'Can't you behave decently like these other children?' Hira Lal, who had been hovering in the background, hurried forward.

'*Bhaine*,[1] do not tease the babas,' he rebuked Ayah. 'It is your duty to keep them happy. And remember that Susan-baba is not well.'

'*Aré!*' sighed Ayah sadly, at a loss to understand why her simple godly tales had unleashed such primitive feelings in the Memsahib's children. She tried to introduce a lighter note with the story of Daniel in the lions' den. But the children had some first-hand knowledge of wild cats, and the placid lions held no credibility. Their loud protests alerted Charles who had just returned from the police station.

'What the devil's the matter?'

Ayah sniffed and wiped her eyes with the corner of her sari while Hira Lal stood silently with downcast eyes. The mission children giggled uncomfortably.

'Come on! I can't stand here all day.'

'Michael-baba is saying some very bad things, Sahib,' Hira Lal said at length. 'The missy-babas, too.'

'What things?'

'Not even to Sahib can I repeat them for I am too ashamed.'

'What exactly have you been saying, Michael?' he demanded.

We were aware that Michael's Hindi was both fluent and colourful; indeed, he spoke it like a native. Terms of abuse in Hindi are common currency, but we did not permit the children to use such words on the servants. However, Ayah's incredible story about the meek lions succumbing to Daniel could not go uncontested, and Michael had used his strongest expletives to express his objections.

Sternly Charles delivered sentence. Susan was ordered back to bed and Judy had to stand in a corner. Bearing one under each arm, Charles strode off to execute justice. Michael, as the principle offen-

---

1   *bhaine*: sister.

der, had a harsher punishment with lessons all afternoon. 'And no talking during lunch,' added Charles severely.

'Thank goodness the Bembergers weren't within hearing,' I said to Charles. 'I can't imagine what they would think if they had heard Michael's language. They think the children are paragons.'

'My, our little chatterboxes are very quiet today,' remarked Cornelia at lunch. 'I hope they're not sickening for anything. All that laughter and fun in the compound this morning sure gladdened our hearts.'

'It sure did,' Hiram agreed. He removed his spectacles, misted over by the hot soup, and polished them vigorously, beaming benevolently at Michael. 'This young man sure has an excellent knowledge of the vernacular. I guess I could learn a lot from him.'

'Really?' exclaimed Cornelia, looking at Michael with unconcealed admiration.

'Yes, indeed!' confirmed Mr Bemberger with a mischievous twinkle. 'And he's teaching his sisters too.'

'I've no objection to a thanksgiving grace,' Charles said, 'but the lengthy chats with the Almighty before and after every meal really are overdoing it. I haven't got time for these protracted lunches.'

During these conversations, which continued for ten to fifteen minutes, Hiram was abetted by Cornelia who reminded him of those in immediate need. Susan, 'the sick lamb in our midst' and the absent Helpers in the Field, received thrice daily intercessions. Since the sick lamb was better and in danger of being spoilt by our hosts' attentions, we decided to return to camp.

The Bembergers had endeared themselves to us all with their hospitality and kindness. After fervent promises to meet again before long, we drove away laden with gifts, pumpkins and a recipe for pumpkin pie. Sister Kumari proudly brandished a new hymn book.

Rikki became one of our best-loved pets. An itinerant vendor had brought him to us as a young mongoose, wild and vicious with razor-sharp teeth.

'I'll never be able to tame it,' I said anxiously. 'But what will happen if someone doesn't buy it?'

Charles was always pragmatic. 'He'll kill it, I should think.'

Urged on by the children, I reluctantly bought him for one rupee. In a surprisingly short time, Rikki became gentle and affectionate. He had the run of the house and garden, disappearing for long periods and then suddenly reap-

Rikki, the mongoose, was adept at handling and eating raw eggs.

pearing. He responded to my calls only and I could seize him by his tough bushy tail while he nibbled a tasty morsel.

He had expensive tastes, preferring mince, fish, eggs and milk. Like other mongooses, he was adept at handling and eating raw eggs. Holding one in his front paws, he would back up against a wall or tree, and standing upright, would dash it through his hind legs, lapping up the contents without spilling a drop. He acquired a liking for chocolate and would turn up at the very moment this rare treat was being shared by the family. Sometimes he would snatch the titbit from unsuspecting fingers and scoot away to an inaccessible place where he was safe from the infuriated loser. We soon learned that the only solution was to give him his own ration simultaneously. Rikki was able to indulge his natural instinct to hunt snakes, scorpions, frogs and lizards for there was a plentiful supply of all these around the house.

When Hira Lal offered him a large scorpion dangling from a piece of string, he scampered off to devour it in private. When he returned a little later with the string trailing from his mouth, we anxiously summoned the vet.

'There is nothing I can do,' said Abdul Ghani, eyeing the patient who was surveying us from the roof. 'The string will surely unwind as digestion proceeds.' Sure enough, the trailing string began to lengthen until the knot which held the scorpion was disgorged.

We had had Rikki for a few months when another mongoose was brought to us. This time we did not hesitate to buy it, realising that Rikki needed a companion. Rikki and Tikki became firm friends, but vied for my attention with outbursts of jealous rage. During my afternoon siesta, they would take up positions on either side and the least movement would be misconstrued as preferential treatment by one or the other. With teeth bared and low-pitched growls, they tumbled around and leapt on and off the bed with complete disregard for me. Then an uneasy truce would prevail until the next incident which might be provoked by the mere turning of a page.

Bold and reckless, they took considerable risks with the dogs, stealing meat from their bowls and taunting them with impertinent sniffs and nips. Even Kim, a pugnacious terrier, learned to respect their sharp claws and needle-point teeth. Their high spirits and amusing antics endeared them to visitors, but they caused embarrassment on some occasions by snatching tasty morsels from the plates, or even the forks, of unwary guests. Thereafter, before dining, I would shut them into their cages despite their raucous objections.

Our reputation as foster parents spread and before long Mini joined our household despite my misgivings about the eternal triangle.

Fortunately, she was of a different species and angrily rejected the advances of both Rikki and Tikki. After about a year, all three went on extended forays into the surrounding country. The more they hunted, the less food they took from us. For a while they continued to respond to my calls, but remained at a distance and became progressively more difficult to catch. Sadly, we realized they were looking for mates and must answer the call of the wild.

'I wonder what all that rumpus is about?' Charles asked, as a crowd of villagers advanced towards the bungalow. He was always on the alert for trouble but these folk seemed far too cheerful to be rioters or agitators. Kisnia went to investigate.

'These men want to give you a crocodile, Sahib.'

'A *crocodile*? Are you sure it's a *crocodile*?' We were incredulous as there was no river within miles. Curiosity drove us to enquire further. Sure enough, a young crocodile had been caught in the local *jheel* and was trussed up with wire and rope, a pitiful sight with a bleeding belly, panting in the heat.

It was known that we took in animals which needed care, and clearly a large reward was anticipated. Kisnia, wise to the ways of these ingenuous people, grinned broadly. 'It is known that Sahib has three mongooses and they think you would like to buy this animal also.'

The crocodile is an unattractive beast of uncertain temper and is extremely dangerous when molested or hungry. Obviously it could never be tamed, much less become a family pet. But if left to these uncaring folk, it would undoubtedly be disposed of in the most inhumane manner. Charles and I conferred briefly. Then he announced tersely, 'I'll buy it!' The villagers were jubilant.

Charles returned to the house to fetch money and his revolver. Then, as the money changed hands, he ended the creature's suffering with a single shot.

The panther cubs found solace with our gentle spaniel.

Theft of young animals was not uncommon, for it was known that Europeans would often pay considerable sums for the orphans rather than leave them to an uncertain fate. When a villager arrived with three newborn blind panther cubs, we suspected that he had stolen them.

Panthers are a diminishing species in India and they are coveted for their magnificent coats, buff-coloured with rosettes of black spots. Skilled tree-climbers and good swimmers, they live in dense thickets and rocky caves, hunting mostly at night. Lions and tigers which are reared from cubs become relatively tame and even gentle, but panthers do not usually respond to handling and are ferocious from the start. These cubs seemed to find solace with our gentle spaniel, Tess, crawling over her as she patiently mothered and cleaned them, but we had to wear gloves to handle the snarling, scratching babies. We bottle-fed them with buffalo milk every few hours but they sucked unwillingly. Since young panthers are fed on food regurgitated by the mother, they could not easily digest the minced meat we offered, and despite our best efforts they became weaker and died after a few days.

Over the years we had collected a number of fowls. Originally acquired for the pot, they had been adopted as pets by the children and had led useless pampered lives. They were scrawny long-legged hybrids like those found scratching an existence in village compounds. All ours had names and personal histories, and were more or less tame. They would stalk around the garden and come on to the verandahs to look for scraps, often disputing with the dogs over morsels. Most died of old age but occasionally one disappeared unaccountably, and I wondered whether it had fulfilled a useful purpose after all by feeding the needy, tough though it was. After several mysterious disappearances, I decided it was time for us to be the beneficiaries of our own flock.

'Mohammed Ali, please make a chicken curry for lunch, and use one of our own chickens,' I instructed.

'Which one, Memsahib?' He could barely conceal his astonishment.

'Almost any one will do. Just show it to me first.'

He returned shortly with a bird under each arm. Their quick procural was easy to explain since one, named Pegleg by the children, had a single leg and the other was obviously ailing or declining through age. I knew that Susan and Judy were lovingly nursing these two casualties.

'Neither of those, Mohammed Ali,' I said hastily, and he released the two captives which, blissfully unaware of the fate which had so nearly befallen them, hopped trustingly towards me and settled under my chair.

Once more Mohammed Ali went in search of prey. I heard a scuffle followed by the flutter of wings as a colourful long-legged cockerel, obviously in the prime of life, raced through the drawing-room in a bid for safety. Other servants joined in the chase with much shouting and excitement. As they rushed round the bungalow for the third time, I noticed Michael also in hot pursuit. The pursuers were soon rewarded; I heard the cockerel squawking indignantly as he was pounced upon. A few moments later Michael rushed in, flushed and agitated, with the panting bird clasped tightly to his chest.

'Why were the servants chasing Cocky?' he gasped, eyeing me accusingly. 'Did you tell Mohammed Ali to *kill* Cocky? *Mum!* How *could* you?'

We had tried to bring up the children to tell the truth and had emphasized the importance of honesty. Now I averted my eyes and said feebly. 'Well, I didn't tell him to kill *Cocky* . . . '

The sound of a long drawn-out screech of a bird apparently in its death throes, interrupted our strained conversation. I felt sick with guilt about the murderous act about to take place on my instruction. At least it wasn't Cocky or Pegleg.

Michael stood his ground, and with quivering lip demanded sternly, 'Which one, then, Mum?'

'Well, not Pegleg—'

My words were drowned by continued squawks accompanied by curses and shouts which, oddly enough, emanated from the office. Why is that foolish Mohammed Ali killing it in the office? I wondered in agitation. At least he could have been more discreet and done the foul deed in the backyard. I shouldn't have done this, I thought desperately. The children will never forgive me.

'Which one, Mum?' insisted Michael.

'Brenda!' Charles' voice cut across my anguished and confused mind. He emerged from his office and seemed to be slightly out of focus. 'This wretched hen . . . I think it's ready for the pot.'

'*NO*, Daddy!' yelled Michael.

'Oh, *God!*' I groaned.

'What on earth's the matter with you two?'

'Mummy wants to *eat* one of our pet chickens.'

'About time too! They must all be as tough as old boots. As for *this* noisy bird, can't it find somewhere better than my office to lay its eggs? I've had a job to catch it.' I suddenly became aware of the white hen tucked firmly under Charles' arm. He strode to the door and flung it unceremoniously outside.

'Thank God,' I whispered. With renewed strength I smiled at Michael and said calmly, 'It's all right, darling, we're *not* eating chicken. None of us seems to like it any more.'

Mohammed Ali made vegetable curry for lunch.

'Does Memsahib want photographs taken?' enquired Kisnia, while a photographer hovered in the background with his cumbersome equipment strapped to his bicycle.

'No, thank you. Please tell him to go away,' I answered sharply, for we had had too many indifferent photographs taken by amateurs.

'Memsahib, this man is very clever,' Kisnia persisted. 'He is coming from Amritsar and has taken many fine pictures, even of the *Lat-sahib*!1 himself in Lahore.'

'Well, who is he?' I asked, weakening a little.

'He is a Sikh called Karram Singh. Very fine photographer.'

I tried to imagine the Governor of the Punjab in all his finery, hand on sword and plumes aloft, posing before Karram Singh's ancient trunk-like camera. Firmly I resisted Kisnia's urging and with a flash of inspiration recommended Marie Simpson. I knew that she loved family photographs; the walls, shelves and tables of her home were positively littered with them.

However, after a successful morning at the Simpsons, Karram Singh returned with renewed determination. It seemed that he was in collaboration with Kisnia, whom he followed into the house as though he were an expected guest, whilst his assistant staggered behind with the large ungainly equipment. Undeterred by the hysterical dogs, they busied themselves assembling the weaponry.

---

1 *Lat-sahib*: Governor.

Alerted by the noise, Charles emerged from his office. 'Cecil Beaton[1] has arrived!' I announced. 'He's recently photographed the Governor of Lahore.'

'Oh no! Not one of those.'

I suggested soothingly that the line of least resistance might be to have just one photograph.

'That's not the point!' Charles expostulated. 'If we had a tooth out just to get rid of the dentist or bought new spectacles each time the oculist visited . . . '

But Karram Singh had experienced difficult customers before and was not discouraged. 'Hazur, if you permit me to photograph your Honour and your family, I can promise faithful likeness and clear detail.'

'Well that's something, I suppose. What do you charge?'

'For you, Hazur, it is high privilege. I give you cut-rate.' He produced a scrap of paper on which his fees were scribbled, and negotiated an impressive reduction.

Charles was not hoodwinked but after some consideration said irritably, 'Well, you can take two photographs of the children. Do you have any references?'

Karram Singh sighed deeply. 'Many, many high and noble persons among my clients, Hazur. But alas! Only last month my dwelling was burnt to the very ground and all, all my valuable references and pictures were destroyed. By great good fortune these few pictures were spared.' He produced a few yellowing prints which had obviously done duty for many years. I dared not look at Charles as we examined the disenchanted subjects clutching paper flowers. The artist proudly proclaimed, 'Sahib can see for himself the clear detail of the flowers.'

Unfortunately there was no getting out of it and the unwilling children were hurried off to change. After much wriggling and scowling, they were positioned to Karram Singh's satisfaction and he disappeared into the black enveloping drape to assess the scene. He

---

1   Cecil Beaton: celebrated English photographer commissioned by royalty.

called his assistant, who joined him under the folds where they discoursed at length, making adjustments for the creation of the masterpiece. They eventually emerged looking harassed and anxious. The photographer explained despairingly that the children on their own were not decorative enough and an extra touch of interest was necessary. With a flourish he produced a bunch of faded paper flowers, the very ones which had decorated his prize photograph, and which had fortuitously escaped the fire.

'Please take up stance, holding flowers – thus!' Karram Singh demonstrated, placing the bouquet in Michael's unwilling hands.

Michael was annoyed. 'I don't want to hold these silly flowers. Susan can have them.' He threw them on to her lap. 'Why can't I hold my gun instead?'

'I don't want them,' Susan objected. 'I want to sit on my horse.'

'I don't want them either,' wailed Judy, flinging herself on the ground. 'Can I sit on the horse too?'

'Perhaps the horse and the gun would be more appropriate than the flowers,' I suggested tactfully, as Karram Singh retrieved his rejected props and dusted them in pained silence.

Charles intervened angrily. 'If you three don't behave, you can pose naked on the panther skin.' This was not an empty threat as we had photographs of them as babies in just such poses. Ayah hurried off to find the wooden horse and pellet-gun, and the children were reorganized. Eventually their ordeal was over and the disgruntled models were dismissed.

When the proofs arrived a few weeks later, we opened the envelope with some reluctance. I knew that trick photography could exaggerate interesting details and Karram Singh was obviously skilled in this aspect of his art. Every minute detail of the wooden horse, including the scratches on its ancient flanks, was in perfect focus but its dwarfed riders were blurred into the background. Michael, partially obscured by the pellet-gun proudly held before him, could have passed as a big game-hunter. Charles protested angrily, but the children were delighted with the photographs of their cherished possessions.

Chapter XI

Out of the Darkness

he Hospitality Committee was suddenly faced with a responsibility more serious than the mere entertainment of troops. Summoned to an emergency meeting at the Woods' bungalow one morning in May, we listened tensely while Carrie informed us that twenty-eight Burmese refugees, including children, would arrive the following week and we would have to cater for them with our meagre resources. The Japanese invasion of Burma in 1942 prompted a mass exodus of refugees to India. The more fortunate were flown out of Myitkyina and Rangoon on the last British planes; the rest struggled through tropical jungles or across the freezing and forbidding Himalayan mountains known as The Hump. Survivors who reached Calcutta were dispatched to district stations until further arrangements could be made for them.

'The Deputy Commissioner has arranged for most of the refugees to be accommodated in the dak-bungalow and the empty house next door. That's right, isn't it?' she enquired perfunctorily of Monique, with ill-concealed irritation at having to consult with higher authority.

'*Mais oui*, zat ees correct. Jashwant has already feexed eet,' Monique replied coldly with a little shrug that made her bracelets tinkle. Dressed in a diaphanous sari of rose pink, she looked cool and attractive, in sharp contrast to the stern and practical Carrie.

The pre-monsoon heat blasted like a steam furnace, adding to the tension. Marie heaved her ample bosom under the button-bursting bodice of her WVS uniform. It was uncomfortable enough for anyone to wear the heavy grey *dousuti*, but much worse for someone as corpulent as Marie. Overhead the cumbersome *punkah* groaned protestingly as it swayed back and forth, barely stirring the sluggish air.

'The problem is that these poor people will need almost everything – food, clothes, linen, crockery – until government supplies arrive and funds are available. Are there any offers?'

I made a rapid mental survey of our house for spare useful items: a bookcase, mosquito nets, the portable commode or "thunderbox". There was also a bathtub which had a small leak, but it could be sealed.

'We could put up two or three people,' volunteered Rita. 'We also have some blankets for the cooler weather.'

'We have a spare *dhurri*,' Jane said. 'And plenty of books if required.'

'Would a gramophone be any use?' asked Marie. 'We can manage two adults . . . but no children. We're too old to cope with children.'

'Naturally, we'll help in any way, *especially* with children,' said Dorothy pointedly. 'We miss our own girls so much.' Marie and Dorothy exchanged hard looks, but Carrie forestalled argument between the formidable duo by rapping the table for attention.

Mrs Pinto, fanning herself vigorously with her palm-leaf fan, had been deep in thought and suddenly launched forth. 'My Gracie and Ivy are going to share one bed. Lenny and Reggie can use another one together. That makes two beds spare, isn't it? But Ozzy and Jackie are too big to go sharing. Many times they are fighting in the middle of the night and my hubby is getting so mad. "Stop it, you chaps, or I'll hammer you!" he is telling them. And I have a cot so if there is a baby, he can come also. My Gracie will be too pleased. My, how that child loves babies!'

Mrs Pinto was at her best, her most generous, her most eloquent. 'And I am cooking oll-sorts and sending jams and mango chutney if they are wanting them. Just you are telling me. Me and my hubby are wanting to do anything at-oll.'

'Thank you, Mrs Pinto. That's very generous. And thank you all,' said Carrie. 'I'll let you know what will be required and will keep you fully informed of the situation.'

The dozing *punkah-wallah* attracted Carrie's attention. '*Tano!* Damn it, *tano!*'[1] she shouted irritably, and was echoed by a servant.

'*Aré, tano bhai, tano!*'

The *punkah-wallah*, shaken into sudden wakefulness, strained furiously on the rope so that Carrie's papers were scattered and ash from the ashtrays wafted upwards before settling over the table as a fine film. '*Asthi!* Damn it, *asthi!*'[2] Carrie's shout was taken up by the next in line and the puller relapsed into a stupor once more. A large black spider, dislodged from the folds of the *punkah* by the sudden blast of hot air, fell with a thud on the table and scuttled away lethargically.

Taking a sip from a tumbler of water in which the ice had long since melted, Carrie consulted her notes. She relaxed and lit a cigarette, a sign for others to do the same. At that point the Woods' bearer announced that the mission memsahib had arrived and was waiting outside.

'Well, show her in, Hafiz. Don't keep her waiting in the sun.'

With her topee secured by a large red bow under her chin and guinea-fowl feathers projecting from both sides like long ears, Mrs Bemberger was reminiscent of a Spanish pack-donkey. She bared her teeth in a friendly grin and brayed, 'Good day to you kind folk. Pardon me for being late.' She removed her impressive headgear with a flourish. 'I got your notification just three days ago, Mrs Wood. It arrived on the same day that Mr Bemburger heard that his dear mother had passed away back home.'

We all murmured our sympathy. 'It's very good of you to come under the circumstances, Mrs Bemburger,' said Carrie. 'We're all very sorry to hear of your sad loss . . . it must have been a great shock.'

---

1 *Tano!* Pull!
2 *Asthi!* Slowly!

'Why, no! It was quite a relief, you understand. The old lady was ninety-two and declining fast.'

Uncharacteristically at a loss for words, Carrie tapped her teeth with the end of her pencil. At length she said, 'Well, thank you anyway. We'd be grateful for any help you can give.'

'Well, Honey, you can count on us in this time of trial. Would you like Mr Bemburger to conduct a little prayer meeting to hearten the poor folk when they arrive?'

'Umm . . . it's a good idea. But most of them are Burmese and they may not understand.'

'Well, the dear Lord will bless them orl the same. Just leave it to Mr Bemburger. And how long do you expect them to stay?'

'Until the end of the War, I suppose. Who can say when that will be?'

The Midnapore cyclone which devastated much of West Bengal in 1942 resulted in heavy crop losses and an acute food crisis. The Government's efforts to forestall the famine by importing rice from Burma were foiled by the Japanese conquest of Burma and the threatened invasion of Bengal. It was estimated that almost three million people, including Burmese refugees, died as a direct result of famine, constituting one of the major human tragedies of the War. Rice and other grains were hoarded by the wealthy of the upper castes and unscrupulous *bunyias*[1] made huge profits while the poor starved. Although the Government seized all available supplies to store in guarded go-downs[2] and imposed strict rationing, the shortage was so critical in some areas that no countermeasures were effective. The problem was aggravated by the strict prohibitions imposed by certain castes; no substitutes for the usual food were permitted. Rahi, the *punkah-wallah* whom we sometimes engaged during the hot weather, stubbornly refused to eat unfamiliar food. The emaciated little

---

1 *bunyias*: shopkeepers.
2 go-downs: warehouses for storing goods.

woman sat silently on the verandah pulling the *punkah* hour after hour without resting – unlike less assiduous *wallahs* who reclined with the rope tied to their toes. She occasionally sipped water from a brass *lota*, but politely and firmly refused all food, even rice. The servants explained that she ate only curried vegetables and *jawar*, a locally-grown grain pounded and kneaded into chapattis. Most people found *jawar* bitter and unpalatable, a poor alternative to wheat or rice, but Rahi had always eaten it and would rather have starved than try anything else.

A small welcoming party waited at the dak-bungalow for the refugees to arrive. Even at ten o'clock in the morning the heat was oppressive; by midday the temperature would soar to a punishing hundred and ten degrees. Fitful gusts of dust-laden wind scattered leaves and debris but offered little relief. We sat in the deep shade of a banyan tree, sipping iced drinks.

'I can't imagine why the bus is so late,' Carrie said irritably. 'It's only twenty-five miles from the station and the train was due hours ago.'

Mrs Pinto looked up and said darkly, 'You can't trust these drivers, I'm telling you.'

'Nonsense! He was given strict instructions not to delay. There must be an explanation.'

Unruffled, Mrs Pinto returned to her confidential exchanges with Mrs da Silva, the Goanese wife of the Reserve Inspector of Police, as they watched their combined brood of half-a-dozen playing nearby. 'I dunno what-oll they get up to when I'm not watching. I have to keep a sharp lookout oll the time. So nortee kids are. Up to oll-sorts, isn't it Millee?' Milly nodded agreement. I wondered uneasily if my three were also up to all-sorts – running around in the sun without topees and keeping Ayah fully occupied.

'Well, if the bus doesn't arrive soon, I'm off!' Dorothy fanned herself ineffectually with a leaf. 'This heat's making me feel sick. And I could do with a *real* drink.'

'For Heaven's sake, be patient,' Carrie reprimanded. 'Just imagine how much worse it is for the refugees – after all *they've* been through.'

The tension was mercifully relieved by the staccato chug, chug, chug of the bus, two hours late. In its dilapidated state, it was remarkable that it had arrived at all. Clearing his throat raucously, the driver launched into a voluble explanation to no-one in particular. There had been a puncture and, unaided, he had changed one worn tyre for another. Then the engine had become overheated and he had to wait for it to cool down. At the river, the overladen bus got bogged down and everyone had to climb out and push it, and . . .

Clutching untidy bundles, the travel-worn passengers disembarked mechanically, for this was just another meaningless sojourn in their rough passage. We moved forward to greet them, feeling inadequate and tongue-tied. Mrs Pinto led the way, and clasping the first child she saw to her maternal bosom, she crooned encouragingly, 'Come with Auntee!' Clucking soothingly and ignoring his backward glances, she led him gently but firmly to the bungalow, and the motley party followed.

Carrie addressed them formally. 'Welcome to Rampur. We want you to be comfortable and happy. Please ask if there is anything you need.'

The subdued party, drained of all emotion, made no response. Mrs Pinto intervened in her inimitable way. 'Oh my! What a long way you've come. From Burma, just fancee. You must be thirstee. There's some nice cold bael sherbert. Would anyone like some?' This invitation produced the desired effect. Our guests relaxed while we offered glasses of the pleasant, refreshing drink made from bael[1] by Mohammed Ali.

A wizened little Burmese woman took a small clock from her bag and placed it on the mantlepiece where it ticked loudly, seeming to

---

1   bael: fruit of the rue tree. It has a sweet smell and tastes like an orange, and is highly prized by Indians for its medicinal properties. The tree, which has fragrant white flowers, is sacred and is often planted in temple gardens.

bridge the gap between Burma and a strange bungalow in the middle of India.

'Thank you,' she said simply, with tears in her eyes. 'It's just like home.'

The refugees were generously provided for by the whole community until funds were made available by the British Government and supplies arrived. Resigned and uncomplaining, they were humbly appreciative of the smallest effort. They came from Prome, Toungoo and Rangoon in Southern Burma and had fled during the invasion. During the following months, their remarkable stories unfolded.

Ted and Doreen Passek had a noisy, cheerful brood of six. Ted had worked on the railway in Burma and was now trying to find a job with the Indian Railways. When speaking about their recent experiences the good-humoured Ted became bitter and resentful. 'I *hate* the Chinese,' he remarked flatly.

'But why the Chinese?' questioned Charles. 'They were your allies in Burma. I thought it was the Japs who ousted you.'

'No, it was the Chinese in our case. They turned us out and took everything. The day before we were due to leave, Doreen and I were packing – just a few small things because we were flying. We were going to bury the silver and valuables in a corner of the compound in case we went back one day. Suddenly we heard banging on the door and when we opened it, there were three Chinese with machine-guns. At first we weren't afraid because we thought they were our allies. They had been fighting the Japs . . .' His voice tailed off as he relived the painful scene, his face contorted with hate.

'But we soon realized they were *not* friends. They looked cruel and we were frightened. The leader told us to get out. I explained that we were packing and we would be ready in an hour. But he raised his gun and said, "We come, you go. *Now!* You take *nothing!*" He aimed at our little dog and shot it in front of us. The children started screaming. We just picked up the youngest, pushed the others in front of us and walked down the drive as quickly as we could. We could take nothing, *nothing* at all. When we looked back we saw them opening the small parcels we had packed, special little things . . . jewellery, souvenirs. They were filling their pockets and laughing. One of them kicked the dog's body. Another urinated against a chair.'

Ted paused, and gulped a few times before he went on. 'It would have been better with the Japs. We could have gone to live in my Aunt's village. But we were too late. We lost everything. Do you see now why we hate the Chinese?'

Madame Blacquière had been compelled to leave her Burmese husband and their village home near Rangoon during the invasion. As a Frenchwoman, she risked detection since she refused to live and dress like the locals. She and her sixteen-year-old daughter, Jeanne, left hastily for the airport hoping for seats on a rescue plane.

Fighting intensified in the city and planes were unable to land. Together with many others, Jeanne and her mother hid and waited in the surrounding jungle, ready to disperse if troops appeared. They sold their few belongings to buy food from the locals. Some who were encumbered with possessions dumped or hid them around the airport. Each day more anxious people appeared and angry arguments broke out as they jostled for places in the queue for the non-existent plane. After several harrowing weeks, when the Blacquières were on the point of returning home, a plane landed and they were hustled into it.

Disorientated and desperately homesick, Jeanne and her mother were waiting hopefully for the day when they could return to their home and beloved relations.

Like many others, Iris Lawson's problems had begun one morning in 1942 when the Japanese surrounded Rangoon and cut off the airport. With no time to make preparations, she took only a small backpack and her beloved little Pekingese, Chen, and joined a group of refugees in the long trek to India.

'The Chinese *eat* dogs,' she said with a shudder, and added ruefully, 'I'm glad the Passeks' dog was shot. At least it had a quick and painless death.'

'How did you know where to go? Which path to follow?' I asked. It seemed incredible that they had found their way for hundreds of miles through dense jungle and across rugged mountains.

She had been asked the same questions many times and her replies were mechanical. 'Finding your way is not difficult when there are many people . . . a path is worn, possessions abandoned along the way. And there are bodies, the smell of corpses . . . '

Their small group joined others until there were hundreds. They kept going in a long slow procession, day after day in the sticky pre-monsoon heat, carrying on their backs the very young and the very old. They were driven on by the fear of pursuit and exposure by hostile villagers, and the realization that their strength and health could not last indefinitely.

Numbed by exhaustion and despair, there was no argument, no complaint, no noise. Everybody shared money, food and clothes. Nothing unnecessary was carried and possessions, once cherished, were dumped in streams. Those with guns shot game for the pot; when ammunition and money ran out they stole chickens and eggs or begged from villagers. The feeble, ill or exhausted had to be left behind to recover or perhaps to die; the fortunate ones were looked after by friendly villagers until they could continue. Malaria, dysentery, blackwater fever and other illnesses took their toll and venomous snakes claimed many lives.

Iris developed dysentery and remained behind to rest in a secluded place by a stream. A young British conscript, Stuart Dale, who had been parted from his company during the invasion and had joined the procession of refugees leaving Burma, stayed behind with her. Although he was also sickening and weak, he realized the importance of moving on quickly and urged her to continue. Iris was too weak to walk but Stuart was merciless. He dragged her with a rope of lianas attached to his waist and carried the dog in a sling on his back. Goaded by his accusations of defeatism, she stumbled after him. They staggered on through the jungle for days, easy victims for wild animals. Plagued by mosquitoes and gluttonous leeches, and with very little food, their strength was ebbing away. To Iris, death was inevitable and would be welcome; it was simply a matter of time until she was just another corpse along the way. But Stuart was indomitable. With remarkable courage and tenacity he struggled on dragging Iris with him, resting frequently.

They were at their lowest ebb when they came across a dying man, delirious with fever, whom Iris recognized as her former employer in Rangoon. As they rested beside him, bathing his face with cool water, he regained consciousness for a few moments and recognized his secretary.

'Iris,' he said faintly, 'please take down this memo and see that it is sent pronto.'

'Yes, sir,' she replied gently, with tears steaming down her face. 'Don't worry, I'll see that it's done.' He closed his eyes and died, smiling peacefully.

That was the turning-point for Iris. The fever subsided; she became stronger, more positive and determined. They emerged from the jungle and walking became easier. Friendly villagers in a hill station welcomed them and they learned that other refugees had recently sheltered there. A few days' rest and plenty of food gave them the strength to continue, and they were spurred on by the knowledge that the Indian border was just a few miles ahead.

It was during this time that Iris and Stuart realized their love for each other. After all they had endured, their lives seemed incomplete without each other. They made tentative plans for the future: after the War, or as soon as it was possible, they would get married.

'Have you heard from Stuart recently?' I asked Iris some weeks after her arrival.

'Yes. He has been posted to a regiment near Calcutta. I don't know when I'll see him again.' Her eyes filled with tears.

'I'm sorry. It's been so hard for you. And no-one knows when all this uncertainty will end.'

'The problem is . . . well . . . I'm afraid that he'll reject me when . . .'

'Surely not! He really seems to love you and you've been through so much together.'

'You don't understand, Brenda.' She paused to take a grip on herself. 'You see, Stuart doesn't know that I'm Eurasian. My father is English and I have his colouring. My mother's Burmese.' Certainly, Iris' fair complexion, blonde hair and blue eyes gave no hint of her mixed blood. 'I should have told him before but it didn't seem to be important. We needed each other so much while we were ill and struggling through the jungle. But now I'm afraid of losing him.'

'If he really loves you, your race and family won't matter,' I said gently, but without conviction, for I realized the sad implications. The British administration strongly disapproved of marriages between the English and Asians and there were undeniable social taboos against people of mixed races.

She shook her head sadly. With a flash of intuition, I said provocatively, 'Are you *ashamed* of being Burmese?'

'Of course not!' she retorted angrily. 'How can you suggest such a thing?' I imagined that her response was similar to the reaction that had made her rally to Stuart's provocation when she had been dying of dysentery.

'Then you must get Stuart to meet your family, Iris. Remember, he loved you enough to risk his life for you and he won't let you go easily. Anyway, you'll be better off without him if he can't accept you for what you are.'

'You're right, Brenda. It's a risk I have to take,' she said tearfully. 'I *will* tell him about my family as soon as possible.'

Shortly afterwards, Iris left to find work in Calcutta where she could be near Stuart. I felt sure she would write to me if there were a happy resolution. Her long silence seemed ominous and I felt deeply concerned. It was a difficult situation for Stuart as his career and whole life could be affected by such a partnership: promotion withheld, ostracized by family and friends and their own relationship put under strain. However I knew that Stuart, who had shown so much courage and determination, would make a very careful decision.

When I received a letter from Iris two years later, after the War, telling me of their marriage, I was overjoyed. 'Both our families are happy and proud,' she said simply. 'Stuart received an award for his bravery and has been made a sergeant.'

Chapter XII

Posh People

By October the rains had abated and the weather was pleasantly cool. After months of being confined indoors by heavy rain and oppressive heat, people made the most of the cooler weather. Officials welcomed the chance to escape from the red tape and drudgery of the office and tour their districts. The annual Tour was an essential duty for officers in almost every occupation. It was the ideal combination of work and pleasure, for although life slowed down to a leisurely pace, important work was being done. There was also opportunity for *shikar*[1] at the campsites, fishing or shooting for the pot to relieve the monotony of camp fare.

High-ranking officers went on tours of inspection of their district stations. In some cases, generous travelling allowances provided the incentive for leisurely, extended tours. Deputy Inspector-General Barrington, an elderly bachelor, was one such old-stager who was known to pull rank so as to cover the best of the *shikar* during his inspection tours. For many years he had spent the greater part of his working day engaged in various forms of exercise, apparently to the great advantage of the service.

'Keep your mouth shut and your bowels open!' he advised Charles on his arrival in Rampur. 'You should start the day with a walk before breakfast. It works up an appetite, you know.' Accordingly, the first

---

1 *shikar*: sport, especially shooting and fishing.

morning they rose at dawn for a brisk five-mile walk, after which our guest settled down to a unhurried breakfast.

Charles realized that heavy demands would be made on his time by his senior officer. He had recently returned from his own onerous tour and had a great backlog of work. 'Will you excuse me, Sir? I have some pressing paperwork to attend to.'

'Very foolish to miss breakfast, of course.'

'Yes, Sir, but I may not have an opportunity to do it later.'

'Well, you really should be more organized. Shouldn't be necessary to forego meals to keep up.'

Charles did not let the aspersion go uncontested. 'After breakfast would you like to look through some reports in my office?' He knew his records were meticulous and would stand up to scrutiny.

'Quite unnecessary. More important to re-acquaint myself with the area.' The portly Deputy Inspector-General rose heavily from the breakfast table. 'What about some snipe shooting? I remember there used to be a *jheel* nearby.'

'I'm afraid you'll be disappointed. The duck and snipe have long since been shot out.'

But he was intent on recapturing his faraway youth. 'Well, no harm in looking since there's time to spare. Takes me back, you know.'

In the absence of targets, they contented themselves with a refreshing swim in the *jheel*, returning for preprandial drinks and an extended lunch. 'Time for a short siesta,' announced Barrington, stifling a yawn. 'Important to rest as well as work. Makes for efficiency, old boy. I hope you're going to take forty winks, too.'

'Indeed, Sir.'

At least Charles was afforded the opportunity of catching up with arrears of work while the Deputy Inspector-General enjoyed a prolonged gin-soaked slumber. Barrington arose refreshed, dressed in tennis whites and eager for tea.

'Nothing like a little catnap to get into action for the evening. I take it you play tennis?'

'Occasionally, when I have time.' At least tennis was a useful occupational stop-gap for harassed and overworked juniors who were hard-pressed to entertain their eminent guests.

'Well, I'll see you at the club at five o'clock. Punctuality says a great deal, of course.'

Charles was half an hour late and Barrington, who had already played a couple of sets, was waiting with ill-concealed impatience. Charles had been arbitrating a bitter dispute between a *zemindar* and a cattle thief. However, he realized that his appraisal depended not on his handling of this important matter, nor indeed on the management of his police duties in general, but on the provision of well-organized and pleasurable entertainment for his senior officer. Perhaps his sullied reputation could be redeemed by his performance on the tennis court.

'Charles had better be my partner,' said Barrington patronisingly. At match point after three strong sets, their opponents scored the winning shot.

'A good game,' said Charles enthusiastically. 'Thank you, Sir.'

'Not bad. Not bad. You'll improve with practice. Just a matter of control, like everything else of course. Come and have a drink on me.'

The inventive Mohammed Ali and I had used all the ruses in the book to enhance the uninteresting ingredients for the meal. But our time-consuming efforts were lost on our visitor, for after several *burra-pegs* he was undiscerning. However, our friends were appreciative since any variation from the normal was regarded as an admirable achievement. Shortly after dinner, the Deputy Inspector-General, satiated and exhausted by his day's labours, dismissed the guests with a peremptory gesture.

'Early to bed, early to rise, and all that . . . Must be efficient in the morning.'

But Charles returned to his desk for a few hours. Struggling to rise the following morning after only a few hours' sleep, he faced the reprimand of his superior officer who was refreshed and raring to go once more. 'Overslept, did you? I tell you, old boy, there's a price to be paid for disorganization. It's a case of self-discipline . . . plenty of sleep and plenty of exercise . . . it's the only way, you know.'

The Carstairs invited the whole community to a dinner party in honour of Bernard Boxer-Bell, a senior official in the Public Works' Department. Not that officers in the PWD were necessarily highly regarded, but it was to the great advantage of the community to be in their favour. The redecoration of one's bungalow or the rebuilding of a long-condemned *bobajee-khana*, or simply the repair of a leaking roof, could be speeded up by the mere stroke of a high-ranking officer's pen.

Such an important community event necessitated sharing ideas and resources. Jane sent an urgent appeal for crockery, cutlery and accessories. Could anyone offer the assistance of their cook or bearer? Did anyone have mint or parsley or lemons? She invited suggestions for recipes which might tempt the jaded palates of city-dwellers who had lost touch with the problems of up-country districts. Mrs Boxer-Bell, who was known for her elegant dinner parties, was apparently making a special effort to come to Rampur. It was rumoured that she didn't like her husband to go to such outlandish places without her.

'I don't think she would come if she saw my kitchen,' laughed Jane. 'It was condemned as unsafe and unhygienic years ago, but the PWD hasn't got round to rebuilding it – you know what it's like.'

When we arrived the party was in full swing. Alan Carstairs had forewarned us that Bernard Boxer-Bell fancied himself as a great wit and had a fund of funny stories memorized from the *Readers' Digest* and *Men Only*. He was well launched into his repertoire. ' " . . . and that one," said the hunter, pointing to a mounted human head, "I shot in my wife's bedroom!" '

'Very good, Sir,' said Carstairs dutifully.

'Really, Bernard!' expostulated his wife, unamused.

Boxer-Bell helped himself to another *burra-peg*, and encouraged by his host's obvious appreciation, began again. 'Have you heard the one about . . . ?' He held the stage until dinner was served, drowning all conversation.

The long polished table was resplendent with Jane's best silver and my finger-bowls, complemented by an arrangement of fragrant orange blossom and frangipani. The candles in the gleaming candelabra had obviously been hoarded for just such an occasion. Hira Lal's artistry was evident in the skilfully arranged serviettes formed into exotic fan-tailed birds with red beaks of petals.

The meal proceeded well until the fish was served. 'What sort of fish is it?' Ellen Boxer-Bell enquired charily.

'It's pomfret from Bombay,' said Jane uncomfortably. 'Occasionally we're lucky enough to get it here, deep-frozen, of course.'

'Frozen fish is a bit risky, isn't it? We eat only fresh fish at home. Isn't that so, Bernard?' Bernard was at the punchline of a long-winded anecdote and did not respond.

'Bernard!'

'Yes, dear?' he answered absently, helping himself to a large fillet from the dish being proffered by Hira Lal. Garnished with parsley and crescents of lemon, the grilled fish looked mouth-watering. Ellen pursed her lips. Bernard would have to be dealt with later.

Monique attempted to relieve the tension. "Ow lucky you are to have a choice, Madame. But ze fish is usually good 'ere.'

'Yes, first class,' agreed the normally reticent Rita.

'This is certainly quite delicious,' endorsed Charles. 'In fact,' he added with a wink at Jane, 'it's remarkable that you could produce such a magnificent meal in that terrible kitchen.'

'What's that?' asked BB who had been preoccupied with his next joke.

'We're marvelling at Jane's achievements in the kitchen,' Tom Jameson explained obliquely.

'Yes, indeed,' agreed BB.

'You're all too kind,' put in Jane hurriedly.

The insatiable Horace Simpson helped himself to a second piece. 'There's certainly nothing wrong with this,' he announced truculently. 'You city people are spoilt!' With several whiskies and a few glasses of wine to his credit, he was in pugnacious mood. To prove his point, he ate the slice of lemon and the sprig of parsley as well.

Oblivious of the situation developing around him, Bernard Boxer-Bell was verging on the risqué ' . . . and I was shocked to find my wife in bed with Peritonitis!' he finished with a flourish, and winked at Ellen who was sitting in frozen silence.

Dorothy laughed loudly. 'That's a good one, Mr BB! I would never have thought it of Ellen!' She twisted her necklace of glass beads several times around her finger in an excess of mirth until the tortured string snapped and the beads scattered widely. Reactions were spontaneous. Charles and Alan leaped to gather the beads on the floor. Jashwant leaned across and groped for the loose ones dangling on the broken string and nestling in the folds of Dorothy's plump neck.

'Don't worry, Dorothy,' said Jane reassuringly, 'we'll find them in the morning.' She welcomed the diversion, but the next course was being served and the guests needed to be seated. However Dorothy, more concerned about her beads than the disruption to the dinner party, dived under the table. Tom Jameson made no attempt to curb his wife's exuberance for he had learnt over the years the futility of doing so, and he sat back and smiled indulgently.

I'll help you,' said BB, sliding out of his chair and dropping on to his knees.

'Really, Bernard! You're being quite ridiculous,' protested Ellen.

'Let him be, woman!' The irascible Horace's authoritative command drew Ellen up short, for *never* had she never been so addressed, least of all when she was the guest of honour. Horace drained his glass, preparing for a challenge, and the embarrassed guests searched diligently for stray beads among their cutlery.

'Well, wasn't that fun?' Dorothy giggled as she emerged from under the table.

BB made his contribution in the only way he knew. 'Have you heard the one about . . . ?'

The company relaxed and the meal resumed in jovial mood. The gastronomic treats were savoured; even Ellen mistook the marinaded goat for mutton.

A week later, the Carstairs received a letter from Bernard Boxer-Bell, effusive in his thanks and praise for the convivial party. 'By the way,' he added, 'I have authorized the building of your new kitchen and it will be started next month.'

'Command performance!' Charles handed me an official letter from the Inspector-General: an invitation to spend a few days at the official residence in Nagpur, the provincial capital. It was tacitly understood that children were not invited, for it was a childless and well-ordered household.

Montague Ramsay was an affable man and genuinely wanted to keep in touch with his district officers. He was hindered only by his wife Gertrude, to whom the chore of entertaining junior officials was tiresome and unnecessary. But her husband insisted on it and she was obliged to tolerate it occasionally. During a previous visit, Gertrude had managed to arrange an emergency which called her away at the last minute. Admittedly, she expressed great regret and said she looked forward to our next visit. Now that time had come and she was forced to face it with fortitude.

Two hundred miles of dirt road was a considerable journey for our old Vauxhall. In the mounting heat it laboured resolutely, refreshed with copious draughts of tepid water. Enveloped in billowing red dust, it eventually choked to a halt and could only be coaxed on after Kisnia, our worthy mechanic brought specially for such an eventuality, rectified the problem.

Understandably, we were not at our best by the time we arrived at the impressive residence of the Inspector-General in the evening. We were certainly in no fit state to shake the hand of the highest-ranking officer, much less the hand of his posh[1] wife. Two hysterical poodles, neatly clipped and groomed, gave notice of our arrival. Within

---

1   posh: originally a term applied to travelling on ships to and from the East. POSH accommodation (Port Out, Starboard Home) avoided the worst of the sun; hence it has come to mean 'upper class' or stylish.

moments a bevy of orderlies appeared, immaculate in starched white uniforms, scarlet cummerbunds and turbans with gleaming Ramsay monograms.

Monty, in light slacks and open-necked shirt, bounded down the wide verandah steps, his hand extended in greeting.

'Sorry Gertie's not here to welcome you.' I tried to look disappointed as I breathed a sigh of relief. 'Gone to some meeting or other. Back soon, I should think. She's looking forward to meeting you, of course.'

Apparently unaware of our bedraggled states, he led us into the grand drawing-room while the servants attended to our luggage. Drinks and ice were laid out invitingly on the sideboard, but much as I longed for a long refreshing drink, I could not waste the heaven-sent opportunity to make myself presentable. Monty was understanding and I was able to excuse myself without explanation.

The luxurious purple guest suite was forbiddingly pristine with sumptuous furnishings and delicate ornaments reminiscent of a showroom in Harrods. At a glance I understood why impecunious junior officials, and in particular their children, were not welcome. The plush carpet prohibited the dust-shod traveller. Removing my shoes, I tiptoed gingerly to the bathroom where all evidence of my dusty journey could be washed away. In place of the usual galvanized tin tub, bucket-filled from a smoky boiler, was a sparkling white bath with gushing taps. I tentatively selected rose-scented crystals from the bewildering array of additives and after-treatments, and wallowed indulgently. Charles showed less respect for the opulent surroundings, splashing exuberantly in a brimful bath, determined to enjoy the extravagant facilities to the full.

'Will I pass the test?' I asked, as I dressed carefully for dinner in a new dress made by the *derzi*. 'Gertrude's sure to be chic and fashionable. I suppose I'll look like a country bumpkin next to her.'

'Well, I prefer the country bumpkin,' said Charles. That was as close to a compliment as I could hope for, and I felt reassured.

During pre-dinner drinks with Monty, Gertrude's return was shrilly announced by the poodles. 'And how are my poodie-woodies?

Did they miss me?' She swept in with a flourish, stopping short as we
rose to meet her. 'Why, of course, the Jenkins. And how are Tom
and Paula?'

Monty intervened quickly. 'Eh . . . Charles and Brenda Parsons,
my dear. From Rampur.'

'Oh yes, of course. How silly of me! But you're really very like the
Jenkins. Aren't they Monty?'

Monty coughed uncomfortably, recalling the Jenkins who were
two decades older, grey-haired and considerably larger than ourselves. 'Well, it hadn't occurred to me, my dear . . .'

'Forgive my being late. One of those tiresome committee meetings,
you know. And Lady Tremayne *insisted* that I should go round for a
little drink afterwards. She's the wife of the Chief Justice, you know.
A very good friend of mine. Very charming.'

Smothering a yawn, she sank into the plush sofa with the poodles
taking up positions on either side, and gestured to me to share the
remaining space. She took a cigarette from a silver case and fitted it
into an ivory holder with elegant red-tipped fingers. Exhaling delicately with half-closed eyes, she said, 'Let's have a cosy chat, shall we,
Paula. . . er, Brenda? I'm *longing* to hear your news. Where do you
come from?'

'Rampur.'

'Oh, yes, of course. There's a charming little guest house there,
overlooking the river.'

'I don't think that's Rampur,' I corrected meekly, visualizing the
dusty plains and bleak circuit house where we had spent an intermin-
able week before moving into our bungalow. Furnished with the
barest essentials, and with more than an acceptable quota of scorpions, centipedes and rats, it could not be described as charming by
any stretch of the imagination.

'Well, I must go and freshen up for dinner,' said Gertrude. 'But
don't *you* bother, Paula. You must be exhausted after your long
journey and you'll be fine just as you are.'

Breakfast was a relaxed meal; Charles and I began to feel as though we were on holiday. Monty had left early for the Secretariat and Gertrude was sleeping late, exhausted by meetings and bridge parties with the Upper Crust. Only the poodles attended, soliciting in undignified manner for scraps. We scanned the menu in its silver frame while several servants hovered around awaiting orders. Since we had a lazy day ahead, we decided to indulge in a full English breakfast while we read the newspaper and mail.

There was a gilt-edged invitation from James and Freda Dalton to dine two days later. Charles had worked with James Dalton, the Under-Secretary to the Government, before our transfer to Rampur. Our hostess seemed surprised by the Daltons' hospitable offer but effusive in her good wishes for an enjoyable evening out. In any case, she had been invited out to bridge herself by Lady Tremayne and simply couldn't refuse.

We were puzzled to find the Daltons' palatial residence in darkness. 'Perhaps the invitation's for tomorrow,' I suggested. We studied the card again. It was definitely for that evening, Friday 6th October. 'Maybe they've forgotten—'

'Surely not. They've only just sent the invitation and they must have had our reply yesterday. Come on. Let's go in.'

'But, we can't if they're not here. What if they return and find us inside?'

'Does it matter? They'll know we're visiting.' Charles slammed the car door and led the way to the columned portico. A lethargic *chaprassi*[1] appeared, hurriedly adjusting his *puggaree*[2], and a lupine animal, which turned out to be the guard dog, sloped off into the shadows.

Repeated rapping brought our host to the heavy wooden door. The bespectacled James Dalton, book in hand, peered out myopically. When recognition dawned, his expression changed to one of astonishment.

---

1 *chaprassi*: messenger.
2 *puggaree*: turban

'Well, well, the Parsons! Come on in. Freda!' He yelled into the gloom behind and Freda emerged with a less than brisk stride.

'Good of you to visit us,' she exclaimed as though we had dropped in by chance. 'It's always nice to see new faces.'

The decor in the drawing-room looked as old and drab as the inhabitants. A single lamp cast a dull light over two armchairs in which our hosts had been ensconced before we had disturbed them. Unsure whether we were expected, I said apologetically, 'Sorry to have disturbed your evening.'

'Oh, it doesn't matter.' James Dalton sounded unconvinced. 'How about a drink? Barley water and lime?'

'The War, you know . . .' said Freda feebly, as if that explained everything. 'We always drink barley water . . . supposed to be good for you. Or would you like something else?'

'Barley water's fine,' I said politely.

'Something else, thank you,' answered Charles firmly. Our reluctant host shuffled to a cabinet and poured two *chota-pegs* for Charles and himself. They stood in the semi-darkness sipping their drinks, while Freda and I settled into the two armchairs.

'Are you enjoying your stay with the Ramsays?'

'It's very relaxing . . . We're on our own most of the time.'

'Gertrude's always busy with her committees and social functions. Plays a lot of bridge. But she's very kind. Just a bit . . . er . . . But we're very fond of Monty. The right man for the job, we always say. Very diplomatic.'

'It's such a beautiful home,' I said with feeling.

'It certainly is. I suppose you left the children in Rampur. Not quite the place for children, is it?' At least we were on the same wavelength as regards Gertrude, and I relaxed a little.

After a couple of barley waters – though Charles' single whisky had to suffice – we were invited to dine. The meagre fare of clear soup, wafer-thin silverside and vegetables, followed by stewed gooseberries, left us unreplenished.

'Skinflints!' muttered Charles as we drove back to the Ramsays. 'With all that money! I could do with a meal now.'

'Perhaps they really weren't expecting us. That's why there was so little to eat. They had to share their portions with us.'

'Don't you believe it. Dalton always was a mean old so-and-so.'

Gertrude Ramsay had not returned from her bridge and Monty had retired. But the drawing-room looked inviting with drinks and dainty, but substantial, snacks laid out on a trolley. A note scrawled in Gertrude's large handwriting read, 'Do help yourselves. I'm sure you'll need something to eat.'

'The great *burra-mem*[1] really has quite a kind heart under her posh exterior,' said Charles, as he gratefully tucked into the canapés.

---

1   *burra-mem*: senior lady.

Chapter XIII

Abode of Snow

or centuries mystics and scholars have eulogized Kashmir in poetry and songs. Emperors and conquerors, inspired by its spectacular beauty, claimed it as their own land and created impressive monuments and elaborate gardens among the lofty snow-capped peaks. Nestling high in the Himalaya[1] with lakes and rivers sparkling like jewels, the Vale of Kashmir is indeed enchanting. As the harsh winter slowly releases its grip, melting snow cleanses the lakes and the surrounding panorama is mirrored in their pure depths. Flower-carpets spring up in the meadows, and orchards burst into fragrant blossoms that yield almonds, walnuts, cherries and other fruits in the late summer.

Under British rule Kashmir remained as a princely state and the Maharajah prohibited foreigners from owning or building on his land. His own palace, brilliant with blossom in the summer, was set in spacious grounds on the lake shore. The British, wanting to retain the use of this beautiful retreat with its bracing alpine climate to escape the furnace-like heat of the plains, built flotillas of elegant houseboats on the placid Dal Lake and Nagin Bagh near Srinagar. Unlike other summer resorts where there was a whirl of entertainment, glamorous dinner parties and dances in a very upper-class English atmosphere, the lakes and houseboats provided complete peace and quiet. Here, surrounded by the majesty of the Himalayan

---

1   Himalaya: lit. abode of snow.

The King's House. Houseboat on Dal Lake, Kashmir.

snowscapes, the visitor felt isolated from the world and at one with nature.

The houseboats generally remained at their moorings in secluded areas along the shore, and hand-paddled *shikaras* were used to move around the lakes and rivers. Each boat was individual in character and size, ranging from modest to palatial. Typically, the rooms were panelled and furnished in walnut or teak. Kashmiri carpets, brocade curtains and elaborate candelabra created an air of Edwardian elegance. The spacious lounge opened on to a front verandah with filigree balustrades and shady awnings from where one could enjoy the panorama. At the back were the kitchen and the bathroom which were supplied with hot water from a wood-stoked boiler. Every houseboat had a service boat tied behind and some towed a floating garden on which one could walk about.

The lounge of the houseboat had an air of Edwardian elegance.

Our houseboat, The King's House on Dal Lake, seemed opulent after our bungalow in Rampur. A narrow, railed timber-walk supported by stilts was the only tenuous connection with land, giving us a feeling of detachment and peace. We were surrounded by pink-tipped lotuses on a thick carpet of leaves which parted reluctantly to admit the occasional *shikara* peddling groceries and other necessities. Lounging on the canopied sun-deck, we were entertained by Nature's continually changing spectacle. It was an ornithologist's paradise where birds darted and dived, wheeled and glided. Hidden choristers in the overhanging willows warbled and trilled and whistled to create a symphony as harmonious and enchanting as any

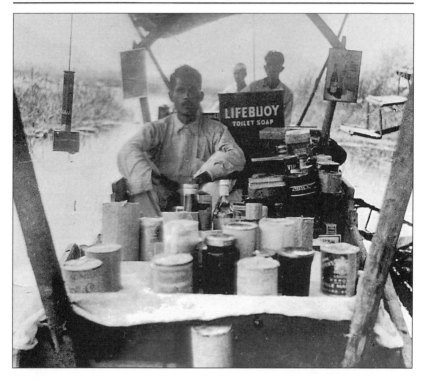

Shikara shop.

orchestral composition. Long-legged lily-trotters stepped delicately from pad to pad, probing for insects. Stately herons and egrets stalked prey among the reeds. From time to time a brilliant blue kingfisher, uttering a shrill complaint, dived from its perch and emerged with a wriggling victim in its long beak. Ducks glided effortlessly among the lily pads, quacking instructions to flotillas of young in their wake. Abundant and gregarious, the teals, mallards and other ducks made a colourful and comic show as they dived and up-ended to rake the rich ooze, and waddled along the bank in sedate little parties. Semi-tame from long acquaintance with houseboats, the ducks eagerly accepted scraps offered by the children. An agonized squawk from an

Shikara on Dal Lake. Houseboats were usually moored and shikaras used to move about on the water.

unwary bird swimming too close to the kitchen, would indicate that duck was on the menu for the next meal. It was served with regular monotony and we eventually complained. Our Kashmiri landlord, an unscrupulous fellow with whom we had had several altercations, was annoyed.

'Duck plenty good. All other sahibs liking very much. What are you wanting?'

'A change!' said Charles succinctly. 'How about some special Kashmiri food?'

'Changes in the menu are not written in the contract.'

'Then we will have to terminate our contract.'

Realizing that there were few prospective tenants, for it was August and late in the season, the landlord reluctantly agreed to provide some variety. Chicken curry was served that evening, and mutton and fish appeared on our table from time to time. For a while thereafter the ducks swam without threat, bobbing for scraps near the boat.

At sunrise the lake is a bowl of burning gold cupped by shadowy mountains. A thin mist veils the burnished surface and the air is pure and invigorating. The stillness is broken only by screams of fish eagles as they wheel overhead searching for their morning meal. Numerous fishermen in their shallow boats are silhouetted against the skyline. The lake is peppered with floating gardens made from intertwined roots and matted reeds piled with rich black mud from the lake bottom. Anchored by poles or towed by *shikaras*, these fertile gardens are nourished and watered by the lake beneath. They yield rich crops destined for houseboats and markets in the city: succulent melons, brinjals and tomatoes, leafy spinach and green vegetables, exotic flowers and juicy lotus roots. Early in the morning the owners of these floating gardens gather at the lake-market with their colourful stacks of produce. It is a riot of activity as haggling boatmen weave in and out noisily plying their trade.

Floating shops rock gently on the water, occasionally making the rounds of houseboats. Other shops along the shore are built on stilts to prevent flooding when melting snow produces surging torrents. Many Indian families live in derelict *doongas*[1] which clutter the backwaters of the lake. They eke out meagre existences from water-shops, fishing and lake agriculture, using shallow skiffs to dart about the waterways. A labyrinth of small canals traversed by wobbling bridges wriggles through the old quarters of Srinagar. Flanked by a jumble of brick and medieval-style timbered houses, these waterways have scarcely changed since Mogul days. A few brightly painted walls are like the unused blocks of a paintbox amid the mud-coloured mess where the other colours have run together. The white domes and

---

1 *doongas*: simple houseboats.

minarets of numerous mosques stand out against the dull buildings and frequent muezzins can be heard calling the faithful to prayer.

Rising early one morning, we took a *shikara* to the renowned Shalimar Gardens, the romantic gardens built in the sixteenth century by the Mogul emperor, Jehangir, for his beloved wife, Nur Jehan. A natural spring feeds streams which cascade over carved stones and play through fountains. The snowcapped mountains reflected in the crystal-clear lake form a spectacular backdrop to the elegant marble pavilions, quadrangles of colourful flowers and lush terraced lawns. Stately poplars and graceful chenars[1] provide a haven for birds and the air hums with their singing.

On another occasion, we hired a *shikara* to go to Third Bridge, a few miles upstream on the Jhelum. As our boatman was tying up at the *ghats*[2] we were hemmed in by little shop-boats. The salesmen held up their goods for our inspection and children threw mustard flowers and lotus blossoms into our boat. Brought up in the trade, the children were perfect little beggars, smiling appealingly, demure yet predatory. Our long-experienced boatman cleared a route to the landing stage, uttering dire warnings about beggars and pickpockets on the *bund*.[3]

The dingy mud-plastered shops along the waterfront, some of them two or three-storeyed, cast crooked shadows into the murky water. The stench from the filthy river, the town's chief depository for refuse and sewage, added to the scene of utter poverty and dejection. At every turn we were besieged by wily merchants dangling necklaces, unravelling rugs and thrusting all manner of goods at us with well-practised sales patter.

Browsing in the dingy hole-in-the-wall shops was a revelation. From the gloom of these little family enclaves emerged hand-crafted articles of astonishing delicacy and artistry. Each little family business

---

1 The chenar (chinar) tree has become the emblem of Kashmir and its delicate vine-shaped leaf is often used as the design for wood carvings and embroidery.
2 *ghats*: landing place; steps by a river.
3 *bund*: embankment.

was a matter of deep pride and tradition, with skills passed on through the generations. We watched in admiration as a craftsman carved an intricate design of chenar leaves, emblematic of the area, on a small table. His shelves were crammed with articles in fragrant sandalwood, elegant ivory and richly-hued walnut, at prices that were discomfitingly cheap. We bought an ivory mah-jong set including four hand-painted counter-stands, for only twenty rupees.[1] Another shop was crammed with beautiful, but useless, papier-mâché trinkets. Moulded from repulped paper, the articles were subsequently hand-painted in brilliant natural extracts, etched in gold and polished to a high gloss using ear wax. The silversmith's shop sparkled with a fine array of jewellery and household items, hand-beaten and decorated with intricate tracery or studded with semi-precious stones. A set of six finger bowls cost only twenty rupees and a cigarette box, which within an hour had been perfectly engraved with Charles' initials and police crest, was a mere twenty-five rupees.

For centuries, family weavers have been producing carpets and rugs in varying combinations of wool and silk.[2] Using crude wooden looms, the lustrous yarns are hand-knotted, up to seven hundred knots per square inch, in complex Persian patterns. Resisting temptation, we opted for a couple of cheap fleecy rugs embroidered with chenar leaves. We avoided the furrier's shop, where luxurious mink and fox furs looked absurdly incongruous in the dirty window, but were lured by a display of beautiful silk and woollen shawls. The legendary pashmina shawls, spun from the fine under-belly fleece of Tibetan pashmina goats, are so light and airy that they can be drawn through a wedding ring. The grinning shopkeeper offered to demonstrate and I doubtfully handed him my ring. Charles watched suspiciously lest, with a magicians's deftness, he substituted it. Having retrieved my ring and paid thirteen rupees for the shawl, Charles nudged me outside. Laden with our extravagant purchases, we

---

1   approx £1.50.
2   Silk production is a major industry in Kashmir and vast acreages are used to grow mulberry trees to feed the silk worms.

returned to our *shikara* on the dirty and abused Jhelum, marvelling at the works of art which had been created amid such poverty and squalor.

Gulmarg is an unspoilt hill station within an easy day's pony ride of Srinagar. There is no wheeled traffic but one can be carried in a sling between four sturdy porters, swaying as in a gently rocking boat. One winds slowly along poplar avenues and paddy fields before ascending the pine-forested slopes overlooking the Kashmir valley. As the rough path zigzags steadily upwards to Gulmarg at an altitude of 9,000 feet, the thin cold air almost burns the lungs.

Situated in a saucer-shaped valley amidst the spectacular Pir Panjal mountains, it is strictly a summer resort with only temporary wooden shacks for visitors since the Maharajah forbade any permanent buildings. The mighty Nanga Parbat, the world's fifth highest mountain more than 26,000 feet high, towers above the *gulmarg*.[1] Extensive coniferous forests clothe the lower slopes and the flower-strewn meadows are ablaze with colour. Numerous snow-fed steams and waterfalls tumble and dance, pure and virginal, untainted by man. It is inconceivable that, in just a few miles, this vital sparkling water will be defiled and discoloured as it joins the contaminated Jhelum.

Exhilarated by the fresh sweet air, we took long walks among the wild flowers and through the pine forests. It was beautiful beyond words and the only sounds were the tinkling water and the pine needles rustling in the breeze.

The Bella Vista in Mussourie had a superb view of the Himalayas, but not without cost. The small hotel clung precariously to a steep slope, and the slightest tremor – for earthquakes were only too frequent – could have sent the whole building tumbling several thousand feet. It was, to say the least, unpretentious. Apart from the

---

1 *gulmarg*: lit. meadow of flowers.

Sling transport in Mussourie. (There was no wheeled transport in some of the hill stations.)

magnificent view of the towering Himalayas, there was little to recommend it. Yet it was overbooked for the short tourist season and the management had to make the most of its limited space. All available nooks had been converted into makeshift bedrooms with flimsy partitions. The cardboard walls and curtains were no barrier to sound; indeed, it was too easy to become involved in the private lives of one's fellow guests if one were so inclined. Mrs Weir and her husband occupied a section of the upper verandah which had been screened off by a heavy curtain. Guests making their way to dinner one evening were startled by a sharp crack, followed by a scream, as the curtain rod snapped exposing the lady, who was of no mean proportions, crammed into a tin bathtub. Being a practical man of quick reactions, Mr Weir quickly switched off the lights and plunged his wife into darkness. By way of reparation for the indignity suffered, the Weirs were offered an extra week's free accommodation in a room with proper walls and a door.

At least we were fortunate to have a choice of rooms and we decided to trade accessibility for privacy. Our two dingy attic bedrooms on the third floor were reached with difficulty by a dark creaking spiral staircase. The children preferred to scuttle up and down the narrow fire escape outside, oblivious of the drop of several thousand feet into the valley below.

We felt it was important not to neglect the children's education during our tours and holidays. It was difficult enough to hold their attention during lesson time at home, and I knew it would require even greater patience and perseverance with so many distractions in a strange place. I decided to start gently with the local scene. The verandah, with its inspiring view of the mountains, seemed a suitable venue for a geography lesson. I drew the attention of my reluctant pupils to the graceful Himalayan eagle as it dipped and soared in the vast valley beyond. But the comings and goings on the road below were of far greater interest: rickshaws, donkeys, noisy vendors selling peanuts, a mangy pi-dog chasing a cat.

'Look, Mummy! That cat looks like Powder.'

'Can we have some peanuts, Mummy?'

'Please can we have a ride in a rickshaw?'

'No! No!' I said firmly. 'Let's look at those beautiful mountains. That peak in the Himalayas is over twenty thousand feet high. Isn't it amazing?'

'It looks like any other mountain,' said Michael phlegmatically, sounding disconcertingly like Charles. The girls joined in the chorus, 'It's just a mountain!'

I recalled my own childhood when I had been at boarding school in Darjeeling. Every day we saw the majestic snow-clad peaks of Kanchenjunga and other giants and they became ordinary mountains to us. The annual school excursion by 'toy train' to Ghoom, one of the world's highest railway stations, and thence by hill ponies to Tiger Hill, was for the sole purpose of catching a glimpse of Mount Everest which was usually tantalisingly shrouded in cloud. After a couple of excursions, the excitement had worn off and the trip became a bore.

'Yes,' I conceded, 'it's just a mountain. Well, let's do some arithmetic.'

'Ah, hard at work, I see!' Mrs Weir emerged from behind the screen of the improvised bedroom wearing a paint-stained overall and a wide-brimmed straw hat. She was carrying an easel, a folded canvas stool and a large paintbox. She usually spent her mornings creating diminutive versions of the towering peaks so that they looked like ice-cream cones. 'Poor little dears!' she cooed, smiling sympathetically at the children. 'It must be so difficult to work on such a lovely morning. *I* believe that Dame Nature is the best instructress.'

She patted Susan on the head and said kindly, 'I'll paint each of you a little picture of the eternal snows . . . a little souvenir. Would you like that? I make Christmas cards for all my friends.'

'That's very kind of you, Mrs Weir,' I put in hastily, noticing the lack of interest from my trio. 'But you really mustn't waste your time—'

'Not at all. Just very *small* sketches, of course. I try to bring the Himalayas down to size, you see. And they will give the poor children something to look forward to after their lessons.'

Chapter XIV

Beyond Recall

The news of the Singhs' transfer was greeted with great sadness by the community. Jashwant, a thoughtful and diplomatic man, was the perfect District Commissioner, while Monique's charming foreign ways had endeared her to everyone. As distances in India are great and communications poor, there was no knowing when we would meet again.

Monique entrusted her pet goat to my care. She had acquired a kid for the purpose of providing milk, but when it turned out to be a ram, she kept him as a pet. Like myself, she could not contemplate the fate that normally befell male goats.

'Zee ozzer people veel eet heem, Brenda! Only you can I trust viz *le petit* Kiki.' What she really meant was that like herself, I was soft and impractical about animals. With the acute shortage of meat, there was no place for sentimentality. We might have been more realistic if slaughtering was humane, but the dilapidated slaughterhouse and the indiscreet piles of skulls outside testified to the crude methods employed. Indeed, skulls and horns of buffaloes, sheep and goats were liberally scattered through the thorny scrub for miles around.

I therefore took over Kiki against my better judgement. At first he roamed free and permitted me to stroke him, but all the while emitted the warning sound of a goat about to charge. He rapidly grew into a large aggressive animal with formidable horns and charged without provocation. However, he had a mysterious understanding with the children and did not chase or molest them. The *mali* went about armed with a stick, biding his time until he was given the order to kill him. Kiki became sleek with milk and greens supplied by Mohammed Ali dutifully fattening him for the Sahib's table, for who would keep a male goat to no purpose?

The ever-solicitous Jane urged me to reconsider keeping him. 'He's really quite dangerous, Brenda. He could seriously hurt some-one – perhaps one of your own children,' she warned gently. 'I'm sure Monique would understand if you . . . er . . . put him to sleep.' I realized Jane was right for he was of uncertain temper and would cause an accident sooner or later.

'Why the hell don't you keep that silly animal tied up?' expostulated Carrie after she had been chased down the drive on her bicycle.

'It's such a waste of good meat!' Marie said indignantly after a close shave. 'He'd keep us all going for weeks even though he's too tough for anything but a curry.'

'Tom will shoot him for you, if Charles won't,' Dorothy volunteered. 'Those horns would make a good trophy.'

'Charles is perfectly capable of doing the job,' I retorted irritably. Charles had been the first to point out that Kiki was dangerous. As a stalling measure I had Kiki tethered and at least he became approachable.

Shortly afterwards he was found dead and it seemed inadvisable to enquire too deeply into the cause. My feeling of guilt was exacerbated by the tragic news that Monique, together with hundreds of others, had perished when the *Viceroy of India*, on which she was travelling to France for a family visit, had been sunk by enemy action in the Mediterranean.

I was awakened from a deep sleep in the small hours by the eerie call of a *phiaou* or lone jackal. The night was warm with a light refreshing breeze blowing through the upper half of the barn door which opened on to the verandah. I lay awake, waiting uneasily for the call to be repeated. A *phiaou* often follows in the footsteps of tigers and panthers on the kill in order to steal the remains, and its uncanny call is like a foreboding. I could hear the usual night sounds: the high-pitched chirring of crickets, the infuriating whine of mosquitoes, the throaty, uxorious honking of bullfrogs. One eventually becomes accustomed to these sounds, but the weird call of the *phiaou* is not easily reconcilable. Charles was in a deep restorative sleep, undisturbed by the night's cacophony, and there seemed no point in waking him.

Charles had told me that a man-eater was terrorizing villagers in the district, killing goats and pi-dogs, and it was just a matter of time until a person was attacked. He had begun an investigation and had instructed the Sub-Inspector to collect information from the village headmen so that the animal's movements could be established and measures taken to destroy it. The *phiaou* called again, closer this time. I wondered anxiously whether the man-eater was prowling around the nearby village or the bazaar where there was plenty of easy prey. I felt grateful for the security of our home, for the dogs who alerted us to intruders and the constable on night duty. The constable usually laid his mattress near the verandah entrance where he could be alerted quickly if a messenger arrived. Emergencies and urgent messages from the police station had to be reported to Charles whatever the hour. Our spaniel, Tess, was a good guard dog and liked to sleep in the bungalow where she could have the run of the house. Kim, our faithful old terrier, preferred to curl up on a cane chair on the verandah.

I dozed fitfully until first light, when I was alerted by the constable's urgent knocking.

'What's the matter, Sagum?'

'The *kutha*,[1] Memsahib . . .'

'Kim?'

'Yes. Very sorry, Memsahib.'

'Oh, *no!*' My beloved old Kim. He must have died in his sleep. At twelve, he was old for a terrier and completely deaf. He had been given to me before I was married and had been everywhere with me –

---

1 *kutha*: dog.

a dear, faithful companion. Well, he had had a good life, and if he had died peacefully, I must be thankful. Hastily, I pulled on my dressing-gown and woke Charles.

The constable was hovering in agitation around the chair where Kim used to sleep.

'Where is the *kutha*, Sagum?'

'The panther is taking him, Memsahib!'

'*Panther*? But, how could . . . Did you *see* a panther?'

'No, Memsahib. I was sleeping.'

'But the panther must have walked right *over* you!'

The constable was visibly shaken. Pug marks and a trail of blood across the verandah, over the gravel and into the tall grass beyond, led to the pathetic remains of the body.

'That *phiaou!*' I shuddered. 'I thought it was close. It must have been following the panther.'

Charles was deeply upset and regretful. 'I might have been able to shoot the panther and save Kim. You should have woken me.'

'Perhaps it's just as well I didn't because the panther was just outside the bedroom. It must have walked right over the constable to get Kim. The poor chap is terribly shaken.'

'Well, we'd better destroy the animal before it does any more harm. It may return tonight in which case we'll have to leave Kim's remains untouched, I'm afraid. Unfortunately I'll be away tonight so I'll have to get someone else to do the job.'

A *machan* was constructed in a tree near the body. Michael, who was inconsolable, was desperate to avenge our little pet.

'Please let me sit in the *machan*, Daddy,' he begged.

'Definitely not! It's too dangerous. There's to be no argument, Michael. I won't be here tonight and I must be able to trust you.'

As anticipated, the panther returned that night to finish its prey. The Reserve Inspector shot it without difficulty and the following day Kim was given a solemn burial.

Michael, full of bravado, was determined to seek retribution. For days he pestered Charles for a chance to shoot another panther.

The panther which killed Kim, the terrier, on the verandah of the bungalow.

'We'd better let him get this out of his system,' Charles said to me. He told Michael that another killer was on the prowl. 'You can sit up and watch tonight, son.'

Michael was surprised and delighted. 'By *myself*, Dad?'

'Is that what you want?'

'Oh yes, *please!*' He was incredulous and breathless with excitement.

'You will have to sit absolutely still, son. Nothing to eat. Even when mosquitoes annoy you, you must not move. Not the *slightest* sound. Are you quite sure you want to do this?'

'Yes! I'll be all right. I know what to do. *I'll* kill the panther!' He spent the day polishing his pellet-gun and practising at targets from the *machan* that had been constructed in the large tree just outside the house.

In the late afternoon, clad in khaki trousers and long-sleeved shirt as protection against mosquitoes, and with a hip-flask of water, he scaled the tree to the platform. The whole household had been alerted and everyone took up vantage points at windows and on the verandah. The servants were hardly able to conceal their amusement, while the girls were full of awe and admiration for their courageous brother.

'Do you think he'll be all right, Charles?' I asked anxiously. The stealthy movement of a panther or tiger at dusk could not always be detected, even at close range.

'We won't leave him for long.'

An hour later, as dusk was falling, we could only just discern Michael on the *machan*. He had been sitting absolutely still, hunched over his gun. This was the real thing and he was determined to show his mettle. We certainly could not fault him. Suddenly, a tiger emerged from the gloom and approached the tree with leisurely gait. Its form was unmistakeable.

The animal was a perfect target for the marksman in the tree. We watched the scenario with concern, wondering whether Michael would rally to the occasion. Then the silence was broken by a strangled cry and the pellet-gun crashed to the ground, narrowly missing the tiger. The panic-stricken child fell out of the tree into Charles' arms as he shed the skin and reached up to deliver Michael to safety.

We greeted the news of Charles' transfer to the provincial capital, Nagpur, with joy for it would bring many benefits.

'Just imagine, we'll have electricity!'

'We can have a proper fridge and *iced* water.'

'And a radio on the mains . . . We'll even be able to hear the news clearly.'

'And there'll be a good library.'

'A thriving club too, I expect.'

'I'm looking forward to a break from WVS,' I joked. 'I simply *hate* knitting socks! Carrie will have to find another keen recruit.'

Hira Lal and Ayah were also delighted as Hira Lal would be returning to his home town and Ayah looked forward to a more flourishing Christian community.

The bungalow was a hive of activity as our belongings were sorted and packed. We gave many pieces of furniture and other items to Mohammed Ali, the *mali* and those remaining, for things that were worthless to us were valuable to them, irrespective of condition. I recalled how eagerly we had accepted the previous incumbent's discarded articles despite scratches, broken legs and white-ant damage. The tubs of verandah plants which we had inherited from Henry Forsyth were now luxuriant and beautiful, and I wondered wistfully if they would be cared for as well as they had been by me.

We received many touching tributes during our last days in Rampur. Even the Burmese refugees, with their limited resources, brought gifts. Dr Pradhan, who had helped us so often in times of illness, came to wish us well. 'Sahib, Memsahib, kindly remember friend of good old days. Perhaps in future years, your good selves will have need of me again,' he said sadly.

'We'll never forget your kindness and the care you have given us,' Charles assured him sincerely. 'I'm sure we will meet again.'

'It was an honour to serve you, Sir. It was pleasure, as well as duty, to keep you all on highroad to health.'

At a farewell party arranged for us by the Carstairs, Carrie was in jubilant mood because she and Fred had also been transferred to the capital. 'I'll be in touch soon, Brenda, and give you details of the next WVS meeting in Nagpur. You've been such a help here. I'll soon have you knitting socks again!'

'W hat are we going to do with all the animals?' enquired the children anxiously.

'Well, of course, the dogs and cats will come with us in the car, and the horses will go on the train with the *syce*. But we'll have to leave the cows and goats.'

'Can we take the cocks and hens?'

I think we'll have to find homes for them,' I said carefully, knowing as well as the children that no-one in the community would be as indulgent as ourselves with a motley collection of ageing fowls.

'Mohammed Ali says that chicken curry is Mrs Simpson's favourite meal,' Michael informed me ominously.

'She wouldn't want to eat our old chickens,' I said, unconvinced, remembering how eager Marie had been for the goat's demise. 'Well, shall we ask Mrs Jameson to have them?'

'Mummy! She's so fat!' he said in disgust, as if Dorothy's large appetite explained the fate of all unsuspecting chickens.

It was a futile discussion and I had to admit defeat. Samsundar, the local carpenter, was commissioned to make a cage for the fowls.

'What is that cage for?' enquired Charles.

'To transport the hens – the children's special pets.'

'Hens? Do be practical, Brenda. They probably won't survive the journey in this heat. It will take at least twenty-four hours by train or bus.'

'The children would never forgive us if we left them behind.'

'It will be worse if they die on the journey. It would be foolish to take them, but do so if you wish.'

The children accompanied us on our farewell visit to the Simpsons. Horace, always ready to drink to an occasion, produced his best Scotch and poured two *burra-pegs* for himself and Charles.

'Dear little things. We're going to miss you,' said Marie, planting a heavy hand on Judy's head so that she was pinned to the ground. 'What are you doing with your pet chickens? Do you want me to look aft—'

'No!' shouted the girls in chorus. I nudged Susan with my elbow. 'Thank you,' she added hesitantly.

'We're taking them with us,' shouted Judy gleefully.

'We've got a cage,' added Susan. 'Daddy says it's all right.'

Marie was amazed. 'You mean your Dad doesn't mind? Well, I never! Why don't you and your servants eat the chickens before you leave?'

I avoided three pairs of eyes, remembering that disastrous occasion when one of our chickens had almost been slaughtered on my instruction. 'Well, we've grown so attached to them . . . they're like pets now.'

Judy emerged with difficulty from beneath Marie's hand. 'Sometimes they lay eggs in Daddy's office,' she offered conversationally.

'I'm sure Daddy doesn't approve of *that!*' Marie looked sternly at Judy who was cowering behind me.

Charles, who had been engaged in conversation with Horace, was alerted by Marie's reprimand. 'What's that?'

I shot him a warning look. 'I was just telling Marie that we couldn't leave our pets behind.'

'You know what I feel about it, of course,' he said drily.

'Well, I hope they all arrive safely,' said Marie, shaking her head incredulously. She had always thought of Charles as a thoroughly practical man. 'Travelling long distances with animals can be quite a problem. Dogs and cats are fine but—'

Charles looked puzzled. 'Yes, I agree. One has to draw the line somewhere!'

On arrival in Rampur three years previously, Charles had decided to liven up the parades and relieve the tedium of drill. 'I'm going to train a band,' he announced prosaically, as if it were the most straightforward and obvious thing to do. 'It will give the constables some interest and incentive.'

'But are there any instruments?' I asked in amazement.

'I might be able to muster up a few old ones. There are a couple of drums and some cymbals in the store, and of course a bugle used for reveille.'

Rampur Police Band giving a farewell salute (September 1945).

'How will you teach them the tunes?'

'That could be interesting,' he said enigmatically. 'I'll start by whistling them.' Charles had an excellent ear for music although he was not a trained musician and could not read a score. But he was not daunted by the enormity of the task. He selected some of our old 78 records – *Radedzky March*, *Marche Militaire* and Sousa's marches with their clear military beat – and played them repeatedly until he could whistle the tunes expertly. Battered instruments were scrounged from other stations until he had enough to equip a dozen aspiring bandsmen.

Using our gramophone and well-worn records, he conducted practices until the enthusiastic instrumentalists had built up an impressive repertoire of tunes. The police force of ninety men, led by the small band, was soon marching with precision and pride. They sometimes paraded along the civil lines, attracting an appreciative audience. The children and I watched the practices and parades regularly, and came to know the tunes well.

'I enjoyed that new piece you played today,' I complimented the bandmaster. 'What is it called?'

'*Liberty Bell*, Memsahib,' he answered, grinning broadly. Thereafter, it became known as 'Memsahib's tune' and was played whenever I was present.

The afternoon before we were to leave Rampur, I heard the strains of the familiar marches in the distance. In a matter of minutes everyone in the house had assembled at the gate past which the parade usually marched. The procession came to a halt outside the bungalow and stood to attention. I listened with tears in my eyes as the little contingent played 'Memsahib's tune', with the expertise and flourish of a professional band.

We spent our last night in the circuit house where we had stayed on arrival in Rampur three years previously. After the children had gone to bed, Charles and I walked across to the empty bungalow to do a final check.

The light from a myriad brilliant stars made the flickering lantern almost unnecessary, but tell-tale rustling in the tall grass along the path emphasized the need for vigilance underfoot. A man passed in the opposite direction, tapping the ground with a stick to scare away snakes and scorpions, and singing lustily to frighten *bhoots*. Above the skyline hovered a vague blue haze, the smoke of a thousand mealtime fires and the cow-dust from a thousand homeward-bound cows and bullocks. In the distance could be heard the tinkling of cow bells and the monotonous beating of tabla in the bazaar. The warm air was like a caress, fragrant with the scents of frangipani, jasmine and queen-of-the-night. These were the smells and sounds of rural India which we had grown to love and which we would miss in the town.

That morning I had spoken to the *mali*, praising him for his hard work and urging him to maintain the garden for the new occupants. Like the other servants, the *mali* was awaiting the arrival of the new incumbents with apprehension since the continuation of his job depended on his reputation and achievements. The garden was at its best, a riot of colour, and I was pleased that I could hand it over in that state. The zinnias were particularly good that year with large blooms of every possible colour. Feathery red and yellow cockscombs stood tall and proud among the wild cosmos and balsams, while orange marigolds modestly occupied the stony patches.

As we approached the bungalow in the half-light, the garden seemed different. With mounting alarm, I realized that vandals had been at work. All the beautiful zinnia blooms had been plucked and long headless stalks protruded from the leaves. The marigolds had also disappeared although, strangely enough, the delicate cosmos and balsams remained. I was bewildered and angry about this wanton destruction.

'Let's find the *mali*,' I raged. 'He may know something about this.'

'What's the point? If he knows anything, he won't admit it. The servants have probably picked the flowers to make garlands for the people arriving tomorrow. Understandably, they want to gain favour with their new employers.'

'Well they might at least have waited till we'd left.' I felt hurt and betrayed.

'Remember, darling, Indians don't think like we do. We are no longer important to those remaining.' Charles was right. They had to protect their own meagre livelihoods and reap whatever benefits they could.

We returned to the circuit house, saddened but determined that the happy chapter of our lives in Rampur would not be blighted by this relatively minor incident. After all, it was necessary to be realistic and see Indians in their own context; to understand the hardship, deprivation and injustice which affected their attitudes and allegiances.

The faithful old Vauxhall was packed, its large roof-load like the dome of a mosque. Many friends, including the refugees, came to wish us well and partings were hard. Mrs Pinto had made delicious curry puffs for the journey. 'I am knowing these are your favourite, Missus,' she said with tears in her eyes as we embraced fondly.

The servants and their families waited politely in the background until we were ready to leave. Then, with salaams and respectful farewells, they edged forward and placed garlands over our heads. Carefully threaded into them were the blooms of the zinnias and marigolds from my devastated garden.

Glossary

Note: There was considerable variation in both spelling and pronunciation of Indian and Anglo-Indian words in different parts of India during the Raj period. Many of the words in this list are English approximations and are spelt phonetically.

anna	1/16 of a rupee
ayah	nursemaid
baba	a versatile word which can mean child, son, father or old man. Sometimes suffixed to names, including female names, as a friendly or respectful address
baba-log	children (log = people)
babul	a type of thorn tree (Acacia)
badmash	rascal, bad man
baksheesh	alms, gratuity; sometimes a bribe
bandar-log	monkeys (lit. monkey people)
banjara	gypsy
basha	hut or small house
bearer	personal valet or head servant of a household
begum	courtesy title for Muslim lady of high rank; princess
bhai	brother

bhaine	sister
bhang	a narcotic made from Indian hemp (wild marijuana)
bhoot	ghost
bhuta	Indian corn; maize
biri (bidi)	small hand-rolled tobacco leaf
bistra	bedding-roll
bobajee	cook
bobajee-khana	kitchen
box-wallah	derogatory term for a European businessman
brinjal	egg-fruit, aubergine
bummalo	'Bombay duck,' a strong-smelling fish which is dried and salted.
bund	embankment or causeway
bunyia	shopkeeper
burra	large
burra-peg	a drink (lit. large tot), usually referring to whisk
burra-sahib/-mem	important or senior man/woman
butcha	baby, small child
chapatti (chupatti)	unleavened bread, usually a small wholemeal pancake
chaprassi	messenger or office servant; orderly
charpoy	simple bed, usually made of wood and rope
chela	disciple, pupil or servant
chelo!	move! hurry up!
chick (chik)	screen made from split bamboo
chit	note or letter
chokidar	night watchman; caretaker
chokra	native boy; young boy
chota	small

chota-peg	a drink (lit. small tot), usually referring to whisky
chota-sahib	junior sahib; customary address for the son of a sahib
chula	stove
coolie	unskilled labourer; porter
dak-bungalow	rest house for official travellers; staging post
dak-wallah	messenger; mail bearer
dastur	legal or customary perk.
dekshi	cooking pot
derzi	tailor
deshi	country; rural; local
dhal (dal)	sauce made from lentils, often eaten with curry
dhobi	washerman; laundry servant
dhoti	loin-cloth for men (Hindus)
dhurri	coarse floor rug, usually made of cotton
doonga	simple domestic houseboat
dousuti	hard-wearing cotton material used for uniforms
fakir	religious ascetic or mendicant, usually Muslim
gai-wallah	milkman
gharah	earthenware vessel used for storing water
gharri	cart or lorry
ghats	landing place; steps by a river
ghee	clarified butter for cooking
go-down	warehouse; place for storing goods
gussal-khana	bathroom

hadji	a Muslim who has made the pilgrimage to Mecca
Hazur	respectful address; 'Sir'
howdah	seat on an elephant's back
jawar	a grain (substitute for rice in some areas)
jharan	dusting cloth
jheel	small lake or pond
-ji	suffix added to names to show respect
jungli admi	uncivilized man
jungli moorgi	wildfowl
kaptaan	captain
karma	one's existing state; destiny
kasoundi	a type of chutney
kauwa	crow
khan	courtesy title for rulers and officials (Muslim)
khansama	caretaker or head servant, sometimes the cook. In a private household, the khansama may also have been the bearer.
Khudah	God
kotwali	police headquarters
kumari	girl; unmarried woman
kutha	dog
lathi	stick or club, such as used by policemen
Lat-Sahib	Governor; high-ranking official (lit. 'Lord')
lota	small pot or vessel, usually brass
lukri .	wood
ma-bap	mother and father

machan	shooting platform (usually constructed in a tree)
maharajah (-raja)	Indian King or prince; ruler of a Native State (lit. great ruler)
mahatma	a person regarded with reverence; a sage
mahout	elephant keeper/rider
malguzar	headman; tax collector (a man of influence)
mali	gardener
masalchee	kitchen assistant
mehtar	sweeper
memsahib	respectful address for a European woman; lady
munshi	secretary or clerk; interpreter
muezzin	Muslim crier who calls the faithful to prayer
murram	sandy soil (used for roads, tennis courts etc.)
nazar	token presentation, usually a coin, from an Indian to an official as a sign of respect and goodwill
nilgai	the largest antelope in Asia (lit. blue cow)
nirvana	enlightenment; salvation; state of perfect peace
nokar-log	servants
nullah	dry river bed or ravine
pan (pahn)	betel leaf wrapped around parings of areca nut commonly chewed by Hindus
pani	water
phiaou	lone jackal
phul	flower
pi-dog (pye-dog)	ownerless dog; pariah-dog
pie	1/12 of an anna (16 annas = 1 rupee)

puggaree	turban
pukka-sahib	gentleman (pukka = thorough or proper)
pundit (pandit)	expert; teacher
punkah	overhead fan made from palm leaves or coarse cloth, and worked by pulling a rope
punkah-wallah	the person who operates the punkah
purdah	seclusion of Indian women from public view (lit. veil or curtain)
raj	rule; kingdom
The Raj	British Rule in India
rajah (raja)	ruler; Indian king or prince
rajbari	palace
Rajput	descendant of the military class of the Rajput dynasty
rooyee	cotton
rupee	monetary unit (approx 13 rupees to £1 in early 1940s)
sarnp	snake
sadhu	holy man; sage or ascetic (usually Hindu)
sahib	gentleman; polite address ('Sir')
salaam	polite salutation
salaam-wasti	to pay respects
seer	unit of weight (1 seer is approx 1kg)
sepoy	Indian soldier
serai	cheap accommodation for travellers; rest house
shikar	sport; hunting
shikara	small hand-paddled boat, often with canopy (Kashmir)
sirdar	commander, leader

Sirkar	Government
sitar	Indian lute, a large stringed instrument
sola topee (topi)	pith helmet (made from *sola*, a swamp plant)
suttee (sati)	Hindu practice of self-immolation of a widow on her husband's funeral pyre
Swaraj	Home Rule
syce	groom
tabla	pair of small hand-drums
tatties	cane or grass screens
tiparris	gooseberries
tonga	a light two-wheeled vehicle drawn by one or two horses or bullocks
-wallah	man; suffix often used with an occupational name
zemindar	landowner, usually a man of wealth and influence
zenana	secluded place in an Indian house for women only